Assessment and Control of VOC Emissions from Waste Treatment and Disposal Facilities

Assessment and Control of VOC Emissions from Waste Treatment and Disposal Facilities

Thomas T. Shen, Ph.D.
New York State Department of Environmental Conservation

Charles E. Schmidt, Ph.D.
Environmental Consultant

Thomas R. Card
CH2M HILL

VNR VAN NOSTRAND REINHOLD
New York

Copyright © 1993 by Van Nostrand Reinhold

Library of Congress Catalog Card Number 92-26278
ISBN 0-442-01229-2

I(T)P Van Nostrand Reinhold is a division of International Thomson Publishing. ITP logo is a trademark under license.

Printed in the United States of America

Van Nostrand Reinhold
115 Fifth Avenue
New York, NY 10003

International Thomson Publishing
Berkshire House
168-173 High Holborn
London WC1V7AA, England

Thomas Nelson Australia
102 Dodd Street
South Melbourne 3205
Victoria, Australia

Nelson Canada
1120 Birchmount Road
Scarborough, Ontario
M1K 5G4, Canada

16 15 14 13 12 11 10 9 8 7 6 5 4 3 2 1

Library of Congress Cataloging in Publication Data

Shen, Thomas T.
 Assessment and control of VOC emissions from waste treatment and disposal facilities / Thomas T. Shen, Charles E. Schmidt, Thomas R. Card.
  p. cm.
 Includes index.
 ISBN 0-442-01229-2
 1. Organic compounds—Environmental aspects. 2. Waste disposal sites—Fume control. 3. Hazardous waste treatment facilities—Fume control. 4. Air—Pollution. I. Schmidt, Charles E., 1953– . II. Card, Thomas R. III. Title.
 TD885.5.074S54 1993
 628.5′3—dc20   92-26278
                                                                        CIP

Contents

Acknowledgments

The authors would like to express gratitude to several contributing authors and editors. Contributing authors and editors include:

Mr. Richard Blanchet	Environmental Toxicology International, Inc., Seattle, WA
Dr. Danial Chang	University of California, Davis, Davis, CA
Dr. Kathryn Kelly	Environmental Toxicology International, Inc., Seattle, WA
Dr. Gary Pascoe	Environmental Toxicology International, Inc., Seattle, WA
Mr. David Suder	Precise Environmental Consultants, Moraga, CA
Mr. Jay Witherspoon	East Bay Municipal Utility District, Oakland, CA

CH2M Hill in Bellevue, Washington provided editorial, word processing, and graphic art support, and Ms. Lorraine Babcock provided word processing support.

1

Introduction

BACKGROUND

What are VOCs? Why are they a problem? Where do they come from?
How are they measured? Can they be controlled? All these questions are
addressed in this book.

Fact

Volatile organic compounds (VOCs) in solid and liquid process waste
streams and hazardous waste materials at waste sites are of particular
interest to environmental professionals in state and federal government
agencies, industry, consulting firms, and academic institutions engaged in
the field of waste management. The emission of VOCs to the atmosphere
is a newly recognized environmental problem. The release of VOCs from
municipal and industrial waste treatment and disposal facilities, for instance, has a number of public health implications, many of them unknown. Included in this source category are the VOC emissions from
illegal, uncontrolled hazardous waste facilities and from permitted RCRA
treatment, storage, and disposal facilities (TSDFs).

Fact

Among the variables in VOC emissions (nonpermitted or controlled
sources as well as permitted, industrial and municipal waste treatment
processes) are large variations in VOC concentrations and composition,
erratic source loadings, alternative process designs, undiscovered and
uncontrolled hazardous waste sites, hazardous waste site alternative

waste treatment alternatives, and new or innovative source control technologies. The VOC sources, compounded by the source variations noted and others, are introducing an undefined and undesirable VOC loading of toxic substances into the environment. Problems with the emissions from these facilities and sites include: (1) odor, (2) ozone precursors, and (3) toxic pollutants. Because many of the sources are located in populated areas, the overriding concerns are human exposure, deterioration of the quality of life, and adverse human health effects.

Fact

Regulatory motives and effective control technologies are necessary to reduce VOC emissions from various sources. VOC control must be required, or treatment facilities will not control exhaust streams. Also, cost-effective control technologies must be available for VOC emissions control to become a reality.

So What Is the Magnitude of the Problem?

Regarding controlled, permitted sources, the U.S. Environmental Protection Agency (EPA) and states have conducted a number of surveys to collect information about VOC emissions from the waste treatment, storage, and disposal facility (TSDF) industry. Data from these surveys indicate that there are more than 2,300 TSDFs, and approximately 96% of the hazardous waste managed at TSDFs is both generated and managed on the same site.

Nationwide organic emissions from hazardous waste treatment facilities are estimated to be approximately 1.0 million megagrams per year (Mg/yr) or 2 million tons per year (tons/yr). Table 1-1 shows the relative emissions from the various types of TSDFs. Over 200 VOCs have been identified with emission potentials in the milligram per square meter per minute ($mg/m^2 - min^{-1}$) range. Many of these compounds are known to be carcinogens. The survey data identify more than 150 different industries, primarily manufacturing, that generate hazardous waste. Approximately 500 TSDFs are commercial facilities that manage hazardous waste generated by others. More than 4,000 waste constituents were identified from the waste data as being managed nationwide at TSDFs. The nationwide TSDF organic emissions are estimated to result in 140 excess incidences of cancer per year and a 2×10^{-6} maximum lifetime individual risk of cancer (*Federal Register*, 1991; Shen et al., 1991).

TABLE 1-1.   Emissions from hazardous waste treatment, storage, and disposal facilities.

Facility type	Estimated annual emissions* (10^3 metric tons/yr)
Treatment tanks	530
Nonaerated surface impoundment—storage	420
Nonaerated surface impoundment—treatment	310
Landfill	190
Nonaerated surface impoundment—disposal	66
Aerated surface impoundment	66
Land applications	43
Storage tanks	10
Total	1,635

* For 54 selected chemicals.

Source: Breton et al., 1983.

What about Unknown Sources?

Unfortunately, there are not representative VOC emission estimates from other VOC sources such as uncontrolled and abandoned hazardous waste sites and related contaminated soils/groundwater sites. This category of VOC emission source includes sleeper sites such as leaking underground storage tank sites (contaminated soils and groundwater), airports, and military installations with groundwater contamination of petroleum fuels, principal responsible party-led waste sites, roadside truck and tanker spill sites, state-led hazardous waste sites, and federally led Superfund sites. The reason for this is that only now are representative VOC emission estimates being made at these types of sites. They have been neglected because they have gone unnoticed (except for neighborhood odor complaints) and unregulated to a large extent, and are difficult and costly to assess.

So Why the Book?

For the reasons mentioned, the topic of assessment and control of VOC emissions from waste treatment and disposal facilities is an important one. It is the goal of these authors to present relevant, current, and useful information on this topic in the hope that all significant VOC emission sources will be studied and mitigated or controlled to current regulatory requirements and standards, which should help to protect human health and the environment. But for this to happen, all of these source types (but not each and every source!) must be studied, and representative VOC emission estimates must be generated so that mitigation strategies and process control technologies can be developed to control and mitigate these emissions.

Are All the Answers Found in This Book?

We have described VOC emission sources, discussed the mechanisms of VOC emissions, presented relevant regulations on VOC assessment and control, and discussed useful emission measurement and modeling approaches including references to key literature. In addition, we discuss VOC pathway and risk analysis and VOC source control technologies including costs of control systems. If this book helps to initiate source assessment, aids in developing mitigation strategies and appropriate control technologies or even just starts the ball rolling in the right direction, then we have accomplished our goal.

ORGANIZATION

We have attempted to present a variety of topics that are key to assessing and controlling VOC emissions from various sources including waste treatment and disposal facilities. The road map to the book is given below.

Chapter 2 describes physical and chemical properties of wastes as well as the danger of incompatible wastes. It also presents a variety of VOC emission mechanism and mass transfer fundamentals for emissions that occur at waste treatment and disposal sites.

Chapter 3 examines various sources of VOC emissions and provides the reader with a brief description of each of the waste treatment units for which VOC emissions are pertinent. VOC emission sources from waste treatment units consist of collection systems; treatment process vents; open tanks and containers; equipment leaks; transfer, storage, and handling operations; landfills and surface impoundments.

Chapter 4 reviews air emission regulatory standards and requirements under various laws and their amendments. Section 30004(n) of the Hazardous and Solid Waste Amendment (HSWA) directs EPA to promulgate regulations for the monitoring and control of air emissions from hazardous waste TSDFs to protect human health and the environment. Under 40 CFR Parts 264 and 265 of the Resource Conservation and Recovery Act (RCRA), EPA has developed standards to control organic emissions from hazardous waste treatment disposal processes. These standards require owners or operators of TSDFs to reduce total organic emissions from TSDFs by the best available control technologies. Standards are being proposed by EPA under the authority of Sections 3002 and 3004 of RCRA to reduce organic emissions from certain hazardous waste management units. (*Federal Register*, 1991).

Many state regulatory provisions require air quality assessment to be performed by applicants prior to the issuance of an air emission permit for a new and modified waste treatment or disposal facility. Regulatory programs of air pollution control have been effective for controlling some criteria pollutants from point sources but not area sources. VOC quality criteria and emission standards are yet to be developed. The Clean Air Act Amendments (CAAA) of 1990 address three major threats to public health and the environment: acid rain, urban air pollution, and toxic air emissions. VOC emissions involve two of the three major threats because VOCs contain toxic substances and are precursors of urban air pollution problems of ozone (smog). Currently, over 100 million Americans live in cities that are out of attainment with the public health standards for ozone.

Chapter 5 addresses the air quality assessment of waste treatment and disposal activities and describes measurement and modeling technologies currently used to develop VOC emission data. VOC emissions can be assessed by using a variety of technologies, including direct and indirect emission measurement technologies and ambient air sampling and dispersion modeling.

Measurement and monitoring methods currently being used for VOC emissions from point and area sources include technologies such as surface emissions flux chambers, wind tunnels, optical remote sensing, transect assessment, mass balance, upwind/downwind testing, and ambient air concentration monitoring and modeling to assess VOC emission potentials. A number of remote sensing technologies and instruments are commercially available or are being developed for VOC monitoring such as Fourier transform infrared (FTIR), differential optical absorption (DOAS), laser long path absorption (LLPA), differential absorption lidar (DIAL), and gas-cell correlation. Remote sensing techniques are capable of making measurements to a level of 0.2 ppmv × meter; and for path lengths of 200 meters, that is a path-integrated concentration of about 10 ppbv. EPA is in the process of certifying certain remote sensing techniques as equivalent methods after they have been field-verified for their accuracy and reliability.

Chapter 6 assists the reader in understanding and applying various VOC emission models and dispersion models associated with waste treatment. Mathematical models are extremely attractive in predicting VOC emission rates from TSDFs and estimating VOC ambient concentrations for risk assessment. When properly selected to represent the source and when used with representative model input data, mathematical models offer a relatively rapid and inexpensive assessment of potential hazards resulting from exposures to toxic VOCs released into the air. Although no one model can be expected to meet the needs of all intended users, reliable models can provide reasonable quantification of their accuracy when explicit assumptions and limitations are outlined. Selection of the state-of-the-art models presented in this chapter was based on a review and an evaluation of all the models available from the published literature.

Chapter 7 describes concepts, elements, and methods for VOC pathway and risk analyses. The objectives of VOC pathway analysis at most atmospheric processes and receptor exposure potentials are discussed. The relationship between source characteristics and exposure assessments is described under risk analysis. This chapter also provides the reader with technical procedures and guidelines to perform the analyses.

Chapter 8 reviews techniques and approaches for the control of emissions at waste treatment and disposal facilities and for hazardous waste site mitigation activities. Conventional VOC source control programs for waste treatment and disposal facilities have concentrated on reducing odor, heavy metals, phenols, and some VOCs. The effectiveness of conventional VOC emission control technologies may not be directly applicable to municipal and industrial wastes because of differences in waste properties, concentration ranges, physical characteristics of the carrier gas stream, and treatment processes.

Chapter 9 presents a summary and some conclusions.

Preventive measures may be the ideal means to minimize VOC emissions at VOC sources. Physical and procedural methods are available to reduce organic compounds in waste before they are released to waste streams and treated at the facility. Regulatory requirements such as use of the manifest system, waste reduction reporting, toxic release inventory, and permit systems provide steps and procedures designed to control potential toxic emissions including VOCs.

SUMMARY

In recent years, VOC emissions and related concerns have been discussed in many journal articles and government documents. However, the need existed for a book covering all aspects of VOC emissions that could give its readers a broad understanding of VOC issues associated with TSDFs, in addition to providing reference lists for environmental professionals.

This book contains technical and nontechnical information that can save its readers considerable time in locating VOC-related data and information in various journals and government documents. It also describes necessary procedures and methods used in VOC assessment and control to satisfy regulatory requirements. The appendixes present auxiliary information that is considered essential to assessment or control of VOCs. The book is designed to serve as a handy reference for environmental professionals in government, industry, consulting, and academic institutions. Graduate students may find it useful as part of their academic instruction in actual problems of VOC emissions from waste treatment and disposal facilities.

REFERENCES

Breton, M., et al., 1983. Assessment of Air Emission from Hazardous Waste TSDFs. OCA Contract Report No. OCS-TR-70-G for the USEPA (Aug.).

Federal Register, July 22, 1991. The Proposed Rule: Organic Air Emission Standards for Hazardous Waste TSDFs. Vol. 56, No. 140.

Shen, T., T. Nelson, and C. E. Schmidt, 1991. Assessment and Control of VOC Emissions in Waste Disposal Facilities. *Journal of Critical Reviews in Environ. Control*, CRC Press, Inc., Vol. 20, pp. 43–76.

2

Waste Characterization and Emission Mechanisms

The extent of VOC emissions from waste treatment and disposal facilities is primarily dependent on the volume of volatile constituents in the waste. Thus, the VOC emission problem is highly waste-specific. Many wastes when mixed with others can produce a hazard through heat generation, fire, or explosion or release of toxic substances, and these wastes are generally considered incompatible. Waste generators should describe and characterize their wastes accurately, including such information as the type and the nature of the wastes, chemical compositions, hazardous properties, and special handling instructions. Table 2-1 lists some hazardous wastes, and Table 2-2 summarizes some potentially incompatible waste materials along with the potential consequences of their mixing (CSDOH, 1975).

Waste treatment and disposal facilities are sites where wastes are treated, stored, and/or disposed of. The waste may be generated at the same site where the waste treatment facility is located or may be generated off-site and transported to treatment, storage, and disposal facilities (TSDF) for management. The types of municipal and industrial wastes managed at publicly owned municipal wastewater treatment works (POTWs) and TSDFs are highly variable from one facility to another. Physically, the wastes managed include dilute wastewaters, organic and inorganic sludges, and organic and inorganic solids. Waste management processes differ according to waste type and include storage and treatment in tanks, surface impoundments, and waste piles; handling or storage in containers such as drums, tank trucks, tank cars, and dumpsters; and disposal of waste by land treatment, injection into deep wells, or placement in landfills (Ehrenfeld et al., 1986).

TABLE 2-1.   Examples of hazardous waste types.

Type 1.	ACID SOLUTIONS	
	Spent etching solution	Acidic chemical cleaners
	Spent acid plating solution	Electrolyte
	Pickling liquor	Spent acid
	Acid sludge	Sulfonation tar
	Battery acid	Copper bathing solvent
Type 2.	ALKALINE SOLUTIONS	
	Alkaline caustic liquids	Caustic wastewater
	Alkaline chemical cleaners	Lime and water
	Alkaline battery fluid	Lime sludge
	Acetylene sludge	Lime wastewater
	Oakite	Lime soda water
	Wyandotte cleaner	Spent caustic
		Spent cyanide plating solutions
Type 3.	PESTICIDES	
	Unwanted or waste pesticides	Unused pesticide containers
	Pesticide containing wastes from pesticide production or formation	Washwater from cleaning pesticide containers or application equipment
Type 4.	PAINT SLUDGE	
	Paint slops	Paint waste from paint production and application
	Pigment sludges from paint production	
Type 5.	SOLVENT	
	Cleaning solvents	Paint remover or stripper
	Data processing fluid	Dry cleaning wastes and other spent cleaning fluids
	Attrix solvent	
Type 6.	TETRAETHYL LEAD SLUDGE	
	Wastes form tetraethyl lead production	Sediments containing tetraethyl and other organic lead
Type 7.	CHEMICAL TOILET WASTES	
Type 8.	TANK BOTTOM SEDIMENT	
Type 9.	OIL	
	Floc	Crude petroleum
	Oil sludge	Bleacher house waste oil
	Refinery waste	
Type 10.	DRILLING MUD	
Type 11.	CONTAMINATED SOIL AND SAND	
	Sand and oil	Lagoon residue mixed with soil
	Spent blasting sand	Contaminated soil or sand from spills

Source: California State Dept. of Health, 1975.

TABLE 2-2. List of potentially incompatible wastes.

Group 1-A	Group 1-B
Acetylene sludge	Acid sludge
Alkaline caustic liquids	Acid and water
Alkaline cleaner	Battery acid
Alkaline corrosive liquids	Chemical cleaners
Alkaline corrosive battery fluid	Electrolyte, acid
Caustic wastewater	Etching acid liquid or solvent
Lime sludge and other corrosive alkalines	Liquid cleaning compounds
Lime wastewater	Sludge acid
Lime and water	Spent acid
Spent caustic	Spent mixed acid
	Spent sulfuric acid

Potential consequences: Heat generation, violent reaction

Group 2-A	Group 2-B
Asbestos waste and other toxic wastes	Cleaning solvents
Beryllium wastes	Data processing liquid
Unrinsed pesticide containers	Obsolete explosives
Waste pesticides	Petroleum waste
	Refinery waste
	Retrograde explosives
	Solvents
	Waste oil and other flammable and explosive wastes

Potential consequences: Release of toxic substances in case of fire or explosion

Group 3-A	Group 3-B
Aluminum	Any waste from Group 1-A or 1-B
Beryllium	
Calcium	
Lithium	
Magnesium	
Potassium	
Sodium	
Zinc powder and other reactive metals and metal hydrides	

Potential consequences: Fire or explosion; generation of flammable hydrogen gas

Group 4-A	Group 4-B
Alcohols	Any concentrated waste in Group 1-A or 1-B
Water	Calcium
	Lithium
	Metal hydrides
	Potassium
	Sodium
	SO_2Cl_2, $SOCl_2$, PCl_3, CH_3SiCl_3

Potential consequences: Fire, explosion, or heat generation; generation of flammable or toxic gases

TABLE 2-2.   List of potentially incompatible wastes. (*Continued*).

Group 5-A	Group 5-B
Alcohols	Concentrated Group 1-A or 1-B wastes
Aldehydes	Group 3-A wastes
Halogenated hydrocarbons	
Nitrated hydrocarbons and other reactive organic compounds and solvents	
Unsaturated hydrocarbons	

Potential consequences: Fire, explosion, or violent reaction

Group 6-A	Group 6-B
Spent cyanide and sulfide solutions	Group 1-B wastes

Potential consequences: Generation of toxic hydrogen cyanide or hydrogen sulfide gas

Group 7-A	Group 7-B
Chlorates and other strong oxidizers	Acetic acid and other organic acids
Chlorines	Concentrated mineral acids
Chlorites	Group 2-B wastes
Chromic acid	Group 3-A wastes
Hypochlorites	Group 5-A wastes and other flammable
Nitrates	and combustible wastes
Nitric acid, fuming	
Perchlorates	
Permanganates	
Peroxides	

Potential consequences: Fire, explosion, or violent reaction

Source: CSDOH, 1975.

WASTE CHARACTERIZATION

More than 4,000 waste constituents have been identified as being managed nationwide at TSDFs (New York State Guide-1, 1986). The waste characterization data file consists of waste data representative of typical hazardous wastes handled by TSDF, classified by standard industry classification (SIC) codes. For each SIC code, the waste characterization data file compiled by EPA identifies the waste types typically managed by the industry sector (using RCRA waste codes), the physical/chemical forms of the waste managed (e.g., inorganic sludges, organic liquids, etc.), and the typical chemical composition (i.e., the constituents and their concentrations) for each listed waste type. Approximately 90% (by weight) of industrial hazardous wastes are generated in liquid streams. The ratio of inorganics to organics in these streams is roughly 40:60. The hazardous waste data are assigned to the specific TSDF locations listed in the industry profile data base by the SIC code and the RCRA waste codes identified for each facility (*Federal Register*, 1991).

Information for the waste characterization data file is available from: (1) the 1981 EPA survey of hazardous waste generators and TSDFs regulated under RCRA, (2) the Office of Solid Waste Industry Studies Data Base, (3) the hazardous waste data base for wastes having RCRA waste codes beginning with the letter K, (4) the waste stream data base for the Office of Solid Waste "Waste–Environment–Technology" model, (5) the data base developed by the State of Illinois Environmental Protection Agency, and (6) the EPA field reports. The data file contains one waste characterization for each waste code in each SIC code.

Publicly owned municipal wastewater treatment works (POTWs) all have small amounts of toxic and nontoxic VOCs present in the wastewater. POTWs that only have domestic wastewater normally have between 5 and 15 $\mu g/l$ of chloroform in the wastewater at the headworks of the treatment facility. This level of chloroform usually will dominate the health risk associated with toxic VOC emissions. In addition to the chloroform, there can be small amounts of other toxic and nontoxic VOCs associated with down-the-drain consumer products. POTWs that treat industrial wastewater have the potential to see any chemical that a RCRA TSDF will. However, the concentrations normally will be much lower in POTWs.

Physical-chemical properties of wastes are fundamental and critical information for waste management. For VOC emissions, it is essential to understand the types of waste based on the volatility of the waste. The primary physical-chemical properties of wastes related to volatility include vapor pressure, solubility in water, Henry's law constant, molecular weight, relative soil volatility, diffusion coefficients in air and water, and mass transfer coefficients in air and water.

Vapor Pressure

Vapor pressure is the pressure exerted by a gas when in equilibrium with its nongaseous phase. It provides an indication of the escaping tendency of molecules from pure liquids or solids. A high vapor pressure implies low attractive forces between molecules in the liquid or solid and a high number of molecules being emitted into the vapor phase. These substances are considered volatile. Liquids with strong attractive forces, therefore, have low vapor pressures and are considered nonvolatile. Consequently, vapor pressure is an excellent indicator of emissions from pure substances. However, when liquids are mixed, vapor pressure does not provide an accurate means of estimating emissions of a single compound because of the additional interaction between the various types of molecules.

As the rate of volatilization of industrial wastes is highly dependent on the vapor pressure of a chemical and its surrounding temperature, it is convenient to have a table of vapor pressures at various temperatures for ready reference. For that reason, vapor pressures of selected compounds have been computed and compiled as shown in Table 2-3. Computerized calculations were programmed at temperatures of 10, 20, 30, 40, and 50°C, based on the Antonie equation:

$$\log_{10} p = -0.2185 \frac{A}{T} + B \qquad (2\text{-}1)$$

where p is vapor pressure (mm Hg), T is absolute temperature (°K), A is molar heat of vaporization (cal/g-mole), and B is a constant.

Both A and B can be found readily in the *Handbook of Chemistry and Physics*. Table 2-3 provides a ready reference to vapor pressures for chemical compounds selected on the basis of their common occurrence in waste disposal sites.

As can be seen in Table 2-3, the vapor pressure of PCBs that have one chlorine is 0.007 mm Hg at a pressure of one atmosphere and at a temperature of 20°C, whereas the vapor pressures of most other organic compounds are more than a thousand times greater than this. Experimental results indicated that PCBs volatilize at an appreciable rate; thus, the volatilization rate of other organic compounds would be much higher (Trofflemire and Shen, 1980).

Once the vapor pressure of a chemical compound is known, its equivalent concentration at a specific temperature can be computed as follows:

$$C_e = \frac{p}{P} \qquad (2\text{-}2)$$

where C_e is equivalent vapor concentration (dimensionless), p is vapor pressure (mm Hg), and P is atmospheric or barometric pressure (mm Hg).

The saturated concentration of a chemical compound at a specific temperature also can be computed according to the ideal gas law, as shown below:

$$C_s = \frac{pM}{RT} \qquad (2\text{-}3)$$

where C_s is saturated vapor concentration (g/l), p is vapor pressure (mm Hg), M is mole weight (g/mol), R is molar gas constant (62.3 mm Hg l/°K-mol), and T is absolute temperature (°K).

TABLE 2-3. Vapor pressure of selected organic compounds.

$$\log[10]\, p = 0.2185\, A/T + B \ \text{(mm Hg)}$$

Compound	A	B	Temperature (°C)				
			10	20	30	40	50
Methanol	9,377.2	8.9547	52.336	92.389	157.095	258.214	411.567
Isopropanol	10,063.5	8.9962	17.010	31.304	55.337	94.326	155.564
Ethanol	9,673.9	8.8274	23.044	41.417	71.617	119.582	193.433
Phenol	11,891.5	8.5138	0.218	0.447	0.877	1.647	2.975
Acetone	7,641.5	7.9040	101.730	161.654	249.146	373.528	546.147
Methyl ethyl ketone	8,149.5	7.9593	46.854	76.782	121.791	187.577	281.276
Methyl acetate	7,732.8	7.9388	93.712	149.740	231.980	349.479	513.308
Ethyl acetate	8,301.1	8.0012	39.416	65.188	104.292	161.921	244.642
Acetaldehyde	6,622.1	7.8206	513.649	767.311	1116.291	1585.572	2203.749
Acetic acid	9,963.9	8.5020	6.507	11.903	20.922	35.475	58.217
Cyclohexane	7,830.9	8.5020	287.937	462.829	721.017	1091.879	1611.570
Hexane	7,627.2	7.7171	67.855	107.732	165.905	248.543	363.143
Styrene	9,634.7	7.9221	3.073	5.509	9.505	15.839	25.570
Toluene	9,368.5	8.3300	12.613	22.254	37.821	62.137	98.997
Xylene	9,904.2	8.1671	3.346	6.099	10.684	18.058	29.547
Benzene	12,054.3	9.5560	1.796	3.729	7.378	13.976	25.448
Pentane	6,595.1	7.4897	251.536	375.142	544.926	772.902	1072.797
Heptane	8,928.8	8.2585	23.367	40.145	66.549	106.817	166.502

Fluorotoluene	9,251.8	8.1011	9.161	16.050	27.098	44.246	70.085
Methylene chloride	7,572.3	8.1833	218.850	346.308	531.654	794.157	1157.172
Chloroform	7,500.3	7.7351	88.614	139.613	213.463	317.645	461.190
Carbon tetrachloride	8,271.5	8.0500	46.485	76.741	122.571	190.001	286.645
Trichloroethane	8,012.7	7.9559	59.280	96.343	151.640	231.861	345.325
Dimethylamine	6,660.0	7.9952	717.829	1074.790	1566.973	2230.192	3105.536
Ethylamine	6,845.1	7.9937	514.859	779.585	1148.556	1650.794	2319.978
Aniline	11,307.6	8.2220	0.314	0.623	1.181	2.150	3.772
PCB (1 Cl)	14,017.4	8.3001	0.003	0.007	0.016	0.033	0.066
Trichloroethene	8,314.7	7.9563	34.696	57.429	91.950	142.861	215.991
Chloromethane	5,375.3	7.5462	2502.405	3466.131	4698.920	6247.572	8161.462
Bromoethane	5,925.9	4.4824	0.812	1.163	1.627	2.227	2.990
Vinylchloride	6,263.0	8.2028	2344.041	3426.245	4884.227	6806.746	9293.137
Chloroethane	6,310.6	7.6603	617.639	905.401	1294.162	1808.122	2474.448
Trichlorofluoromethane	6,424.1	7.5638	404.252	596.686	858.389	1206.524	1660.492
Dichloroethene	7,211.8	8.0871	332.755	515.172	774.919	1135.630	1625.342
Dichloroethane	7,288.0	7.6300	101.444	157.782	238.361	350.728	503.876
Dichloropropane	8,428.5	7.8824	23.909	39.849	64.214	100.372	152.613
Bromoform	9,673.3	7.8754	2.576	4.631	8.007	13.369	21.624
Tetrachloroethene	9,240.5	8.0262	7.867	13.772	23.237	37.919	60.030
Tetrachloroethane	9,296.5	7.9380	5.813	10.211	17.283	28.287	44.906
Chlorobenzene	10,098.0	8.5000	5.104	9.412	16.671	28.468	47.031
Ethylbenzene	9,301.3	7.8095	4.287	7.533	12.755	20.880	33.156

Source: Handbook of Chemistry and Physics.

Solubility

Solubility is the total mass of a substance that will dissolve in a solvent (usually water) at a given temperature and pressure. The solubility of a substance affects the rate at which molecules of the substance will escape from a liquid via vaporization. Substances with high vapor pressures and low solubilities will readily vaporize from solution. Conversely, substances with high water solubilities and low vapor pressures will tend to remain in solution or be nonvolatile. The solubility of a substance is a required input in the calculation of Henry's law constant, which is described below.

Henry's Law Constant

Henry's law constant is the ratio of the partial pressure of the solute gas (i.e., the impurity or pollutant) divided by the mole fraction of the gas in solution. By taking into account partial pressure and solubility, Henry's law constant, H, gives an indication of the tendency of molecules to escape from a solution. The higher the H value of a chemical waste is, the faster the volatilization.

Henry's law constants are expressed in several units that may be determined by measuring a gas partial pressure and a liquid concentration, as follows:

$$H_i = \frac{p}{C_i} \tag{2-4}$$

where C_i is the contaminant concentration, and p is the contaminant partial pressure. The greatest accuracy obviously is obtained at high pressures and concentrations, usually in orders of magnitude above environmental values. Thus, H_i at environmental conditions may differ from the handbook value. A collection of Henry's law constants is given in Table 2-4.

The relationship between Henry's law constant and the volatilization rate of compounds in an aqueous solution is given below (Lyman et al., 1982):

- $H < 10^{-7}$ atm-m^3/mol. The substance is less volatile than water, and its concentration will increase as water evaporates; it is essentially nonvolatile.
- $10^{-7} < H < 10^{-5}$ atm-m^3/mol. The substance slowly volatilizes; the rate is controlled by slow molecular diffusion through air.

TABLE 2-6. Diffusion coefficients in air and water for RCRA wastes identified as highly volatile from water.

Waste name	Waste code	Henry's law constant (atm-m^3/mol)	Diffusion coefficient in air (cm^2/sec)	Diffusion coefficient in water (cm^2/sec)	Liquid-phase mass transfer coefficient (cm/hr)
Bis(2-ethylhexyl phthalate)	U020	26.6	0.0318	0.0000031	0.138
Cyanogen	P031	9.91	0.1144	0.0000114	10.4
Reserpine	U200	4.28	0.0339	0.00000337	0.111
Dichlorodifluoromethane	U075	2.75	0.0944	0.0000113	0.248
Nickel carbonyl	P073	0.5			0.217
Chloromethane	U045	0.38	0.1085	0.000011	10.16
Phosphine	P096	0.19	0.151	0.0000111	22.75
Cyclohexane	U056	0.18	0.0839	0.0000091	0.298
2-Nitropropane	U171	0.12	0.0884	0.0000099	0.289
Pentachloroethane	U184	0.1	0.0717	0.0000082	0.192
Hexachlorobutadiene	U128	0.0914	0.0614	0.00000678	0.169
Trichlorofluoromethane	U121	0.058	0.0862	0.0000102	0.233
Hexachloroethane	U131	0.013	0.0614	0.00000764	0.177
2,3,4,6-Tetrachlorophenol	U212	0.045	0.0624	0.00000608	0.179
1,3-Pentadiene	U186	0.042	0.0912	0.00000984	0.331
Tetrachloromethane	U211	0.03	0.0828	0.00001	0.22
Pentachloronitrobenzene	U185	0.029	0.0533	0.00000617	0.159
Hexachloropropene	U243	0.025	0.0636	0.00000709	0.173
1,1,1-Trichloroethane	U226	0.0342	0.0194	0.0000093	0.236
Hexachlorocyclopentadiene	U130	0.016	0.0621	0.00000649	0.165
1,1-Dichloroethene	U078	0.015	0.1144	0.0000114	0.277
Cumene	U055	0.014	0.0102	0.00000755	0.249
DUU	U060	0.0176	0.0494	0.00000519	0.152
Carbon disulfide	P072	0.012	0.1045	0.0000128	0.313
Trichloroethene	U228	0.00892	0.0875	0.0000103	0.238
3-Methylchloroanthrene	U157	0.0011	0.0501	0.00000528	0.167
Toluene	U220	0.00664	0.0849	0.0000091	0.284
1,2-Dichloroethene	U079	0.0066	0.1144	0.0000114	0.277
Furan	U124	0.0057	0.107	0.0000124	0.331
Bromomethane	U029	0.0053	0.1141	0.0000146	0.28
Benzene	U019	0.0055	0.0932	0.0000103	0.309
Methyl iodide	U138	0.005	0.1075	0.0000117	0.229
Toxaphene	U224	0.00489			0.17

TABLE 2-7. Diffusion coefficients in air and water for RCRA wastes identified as highly volatile from soil.

Waste name	Waste code	Relative Soil Volatility		Diffusion coefficient in air (cm²/sec)	Diffusion coefficient in water (cm²/sec)
		Dry	Wet		
Formaldehyde	U122	1906	809	0.112	0.0000206
Cyanogen	P031	1473	552	0.1185	0.0000133
Bromomethane	U029	1700	544	0.1139	0.0000146
Dichlorodifluoromethane	U015	1450	439	0.0944	0.0000113
Chloroethene	U043	950	336	0.1225	0.0000129
Methanethiol	U153	570	219	0.1242	0.0000143
Ethylene oxide	U115	505	195	0.1329	0.0000154
Dimethylamine	U092		193	0.0561	0.0000107
Hydrofluoric acid	U134	370	179	0.2553	0.0000344
Cyanogen chloride	P033	420	152	0.1213	0.0000147
Phosgene	P095	450	144	0.101	0.0000123
Hydrocyanic acid	P063	321	140	0.1677	0.0000187
Acetaldehyde	U001	360	139	0.1415	0.0000171
Methylethylketone peroxide	U160	302	100	0.0853	0.0000095
Furan	U124	222	77	0.107	0.0000124
Trichlorofluoromethane	U121	223	66	0.0862	0.0000102
1,1-Dichloroethene	U070	202	64	0.1144	0.0000114
Ethyl ether	U117	184	63	0.0892	0.0000097
1,3-Pentadiene	U106	145	50	0.0912	0.00000984
Methylene chloride	U080	141	46	0.1037	0.0000129
Carbon disulfide	P022	121	41	0.1045	0.0000128
Chloroacetaldehyde	P023	108	36	0.1032	0.0000121
Acetyl chloride	U006	108	36	0.105	0.0000124
1-Propanamine	U194	101	36	0.0996	0.0000108
Acrolein	P003	96	34	0.1131	0.0000129
Methyl iodide	U138	116	34	0.1025	0.0000132

interface, and (2) no resistance is offered to the transfer of the diffusing component at the interface itself. The latter implies that the concentration of each component in its respective phases (liquid and gas) at the interface is defined by the equilibrium constant.

The overall mass transfer coefficient will be in the form of a series of individual mass transfer coefficients and the equilibrium constant. The equilibrium constant for vapor–liquid equilibrium represents the chemical partitioning between the phases at the steady state. Equilibrium is assumed to exist at the interface of the vapor and the liquid.

There are several ways of determining the values of the vapor–liquid equilibrium constant. In some cases, values obtained from the results of vapor–liquid equilibrium experiments can be found in the literature. For other compounds, equilibrium constants can be calculated from Henry's law constants. A detailed discussion of mass transfer fundamentals is given in the following section.

The mass transfer coefficients K_L and K_G in liquid and air phases are critical variables in estimating emission rates from liquid surfaces. The values of K_L and K_G have been investigated by several researchers (Cohen et al., 1978; Freeman, 1979; Owen et al., 1964; Thibodeaux, 1978). Two simplified equations have been developed for surface impoundments, based on the experimental studies with slight modification:

$$K_L = 4.45 \times 10^{-3} \, M^{-0.5} (1.025)^{t-20} \, U^{0.67} \, H_d^{-0.85} \qquad (2\text{-}7)$$

where K_L is the liquid phase mass transfer coefficient (g-mol/cm^2-sec), M is the molecular weight of the compound (g/g-mol), t is the temperature (°C), U is the surface velocity (cm/sec), and H_d is the depth of the impoundment (cm); and:

$$K_G = 8 \times 10^{-4} \, M^{-1} \, W^{0.78} \, Z^{-0.11} \, S_c^{-0.67} \qquad (2\text{-}8)$$

where K_G is the gas-phase mass transfer coefficient (g-mol/cm^2-sec), M is the molecular weight of the compound (g/g-mol), W is the wind speed (m/hr), Z is the length of the impoundment (m), and S_C is the gas-phase Schmidt number (dimensionless).

Most Schmidt numbers lie between 1.0 and 3.0, the higher values applying to high molecular weight compounds with low diffusivities. For most hydrocarbons and chlorinated hydrocarbons with molecular weights above 200, a suggested value of 0.5 may be used for $S_C^{-0.67}$; for molecular weight between 100 and 200, $S_C^{-0.67}$ is about 0.6; and for molecular weight below 100, $S_C^{-0.67}$ is about 0.7. These suggested values are calculated for approximation, and the possible error introduced by this approach should be less than 10%.

The overall mass transfer coefficient, K_{OA}, can be expressed in terms of combining the two individual phase mass transfer coefficients, K_L and K_G, as shown below:

$$\frac{1}{K_{OA}} = \frac{1}{K_L} + \frac{1}{KK_G}$$

(2-9)

where K is the constant establishing the equilibrium between the liquid and gas phases, expressed by

$$K = \left(\frac{H_i}{PM}\right) \times 10^6$$

(2-10)

where H_i is the Henry's law constant of the compound (atm-m^3/mol), P is the total pressure (atm), and M is the average molecular weight of the liquid (g/mol).

The mass transfer coefficients K_L and K_G computed from the above equations in g-mol/cm^2-sec can be converted to other systems of units as follows:

$$1\,\frac{\text{g-mol}}{\text{cm}^2\text{-sec}} = 7{,}350\,\frac{\text{lb-mol}}{\text{ft}^2\text{-hr}}$$

(2-11)

$$1\,\frac{\text{g-mol}}{\text{cm}^2\text{-sec}} = 36 \cdot M \cdot \frac{\text{m}}{\text{hr}}$$

(2-12)

where M is the molecular weight of the contaminant in grams. For example, assume that the K_{OA} for benzene is 48.6 lb-mol/ft^2-hr. This value can be converted to 0.0066 g-mol/cm^2-hr, or 18.6 m/hr.

VOC emission rates from waste sources can be estimated by using appropriate theoretical models. Overall mass transfer coefficient can be calculated by individual mass transfer coefficient correlations for each environmental phase (i.e., air, liquid, and soil).

The emission rate of VOCs is a function of the overall mass transfer coefficient, K. The individual mass transfer coefficients for two or more phases must be calculated to determine K. However, the resistance in one phase dominates or controls the transfer rate to such an extent that only its coefficient needs to be calculated. For instance, at landfills or land treatment facilities, the transfer mass for a chemical vapor includes soil and air. Because, under most conditions, the soil phase presents more resistance to mass transfer than the air, only the soil-phase mass transfer coefficient needs to be calculated. Similarly, for surface impoundments or open tanks, a controlling phase (air or liquid) can be determined from the individual chemical properties. This is accomplished by using the two-phase resistance theory to describe the mass transfer within the environmental system. Applications of overall and individual mass transfer coefficients will be discussed further in Chapter 6.

Partition Coefficients

Partition coefficients, indicating a measure of partitioning under equilibrium conditions between chemicals at the interface of air–soil, air–water, and water–soil media, are important variables in predicting volatilization rates of chemicals under consideration. Air–soil partition coefficients, K_{as} (g soil/cm^3-air), can be estimated on the basis of the Henry's law constant, H_i, and the soil–water partition coefficient, K_{sw}, using the following empirical relationships:

$$K_{as} = \frac{H_i}{K_{sw}} \tag{2-13}$$

The Henry's law constant can be calculated by using the following established relationship:

$$H_i = \frac{p}{s} \tag{2-14}$$

where p is the vapor pressure of a chemical (atm), and S is the water solubility of a chemical (g-mol/m^3).

The soil–water partition coefficient, K_{sw}, may be estimated by using the values of the soil sorption coefficient, K_{OC}, and the soil organic carbon content, % O.C., as follows:

$$K_{sw} = K_{OC} \left(\frac{\% \ O.C.}{100} \right) \tag{2-15}$$

Soil sorption coefficients, K_{OC}, can be predicted from octanol–water partition coefficients, K_{OW}, using the following equation:

$$\log(K_{OC}) = a \log(K_{OW}) + b \tag{2-16}$$

where a and b are constants that are empirically derived (Lyman et al., 1982). Example values for these constants are $a = 0.554$ and $b = 1.377$ for pesticides, and $a = 1.00$ and $b = -0.21$ for aromatics and polynuclear aromatics.

Organic carbon soil sorption coefficients of organic compounds also can be predicted from compound solubility, S, by using the following equation:

$$\log(K_{OC}) = a \log(S) + b \qquad (2\text{-}17)$$

where a and b are constants that are determined empirically, as shown in Table 2-8.

TABLE 2-8.   Constants for soil sorption coefficient calculation.

a	b	S	Application
−0.55	3.64	mg/l	Wide variety of pesticides
−0.54	0.44	mole fraction	Aromatic or polynuclear aromatic
−0.557	4.277	μ mol/l	Chlorinated hydrocarbons

EMISSION MECHANISMS

VOC emissions from waste sources can occur through a variety of mechanisms, including (1) volatilization, (2) hydrolysis, (3) photodecomposition, (4) biodegradation, and (5) incineration. The relative importance of these mechanisms varies as a function of source strength and types as well as the physical and chemical properties of the organic compounds.

Volatilization

Volatilization, which is often the most important mechanism for VOC emission, occurs when molecules of a dissolved compound escape to an adjacent gas layer. The rate of volatilization at a liquid–air or a solid–air interface is a function of the concentration and properties of releasing organics, wastewater or soil properties, and surrounding conditions of the air, wastewater, and soil. Volatilization can occur at a relatively low temperature, whereas vaporization (changing a liquid phase to gas phase by boiling) requires a much higher temperature.

Chemical-specific data may be used to approximate a chemical's volatility behavior in a complex waste solution. The actual volatility of a chemical waste in complex solutions or mixtures is dependent on physical-chemical interactions of solution constituents. The calculation of the volatility of waste stream constituents is a complex and time-consuming operation requiring the use of activity coefficients that are generally unavailable for most combinations of RCRA wastes. Thus, in order to approximate a specific waste constituent's behavior, the volatility of the pure substance and its volatility in a water and soil system currently are used.

Volatility may be expressed in three ways: (1) volatility of the pure substance, (2) volatility from aqueous solution, and (3) volatility from soil. This is necessary because a substance's volatility depends on the conditions under which it is handled. Although a pure chemical waste may be highly volatile, its volatility may be significantly reduced when it is present in an aqueous condition or in soil.

Hydrolysis

Hydrolysis occurs when an organic compound $(R \cdot FG)$ reacts with water; the reaction usually replaces a functional group (FG) of the organic compound with a hydroxyl. Hydrolysis is the chemical decomposition or splitting of a compound by means of water, as in the following general equation:

$$H_2O + R \cdot FG \rightleftharpoons R \cdot OH + H \cdot FG \qquad (2\text{-}18)$$

Water, in the form of its hydrogen and hydroxyl ions, adds to the cleaved compound. The addition of water generally is catalyzed by ions and without added ions may be a very slow process. Consequently, the addition of acid or base increases the concentration of hydrogen or hydroxyl ions with a corresponding increase in the rate of hydrolysis. Certain enzymes also catalyze the hydrolysis of some organic compounds.

The most typical example of the hydrolysis of an organic compound is that of an ester, such as:

$$CH_3COOC_2H_5 + H \cdot OH \rightleftharpoons CH_3COOH + C_2H_5OH \qquad (2\text{-}19)$$

Photodecomposition

Photodecomposition occurs when absorbed light initiates a chemical reaction. For photodecomposition to take place, it is necessary to add to the reaction a certain amount of energy derived from molecular collisions or from radiation. In atmospheric reactions the temperature usually is limited to a narrow range that does not supply enough energy for most reactions. Light-activated processes play an important role in atmospheric reactions, and may be considered initiators of most dark reactions by endowing atoms and molecules with the necessary activation energy. The limitations on photodecomposition are set forth in the two fundamental laws of photochemistry.

The first law requires that light be absorbed by the reacting atoms or molecules. The second law states that one molecule of a reacting substance may be activated by the absorption of one light quantum. A light quantum is the smallest amount of energy that can be removed from a beam of light by any material system. A molecule thus can absorb several of these quanta but not less than one. The size of this energy is directly proportional to the frequency of light and usually is expressed as hv, where v is the frequency of light, and h is Planck's constant, having the value of 6.62×10^{-27} erg-sec. A typical reaction is shown below:

$$hv + RX \rightarrow R\cdot + \cdot X \qquad (2\text{-}20)$$

Information about VOCs released to the atmosphere from TSDFs undergoing photochemical decomposition is limited, but it is thought that photochemical oxidation processes play an important role because rapid photo-oxidation is known to occur for many organic compounds.

Biodegradation

Biodegradation is the breaking down of organic wastes by the action of living microorganisms. Biodegradation processes may be divided into two major categories: aerobic processes and anaerobic processes. In aerobic systems, microorganisms use oxygen to biologically oxidize organic compounds. Anaerobic systems do not require oxygen, and the anaerobic organisms exist and react in a relatively oxygen-free environment. Each of these processes can be further divided into suspended growth and attached growth systems. Suspended growth systems are characterized by microbes moving freely within the waste stream or suspended by mechanical agitation. Attached growth systems have layers of microbes attached to a suitable medium that comes into surface content with the waste stream (U.S. EPA, 1986).

Biodegradation takes place when microbes break down organic compounds for metabolic changes. It can be an important mechanism for gas-phase emissions from landfills, surface impoundments, and land treatment facilities. The rate of organic biodegradation depends on the structure of the organic compound, the metabolic requirements of the microbes, and the site-specific environmental conditions.

Incineration

Incineration is the principal waste treatment/disposal alternative to land disposal. It can be a source of both particulate and gaseous pollutants, including volatile, semivolatile, and almost nonvolatile organic compounds. However, incineration possesses several advantages as a waste disposal technology:

- The basic technology is available and reasonably well-developed.
- Toxic components of wastes can be converted to harmless compounds or, at least, to less harmful compounds.
- Incineration provides for the ultimate disposal of waste and thus eliminates the possibility of problems resurfacing in the future.
- The volume of waste is greatly reduced by the process, which leaves only noncombustible inorganic ash.
- Large land areas are not required. •
- Heat recovery makes it possible to recover some of the energy produced by incineration.

Incineration processes vary widely in overall complexity, but essentially involve a basic oxidation and/or pyrolysis reaction. Wastes are largely, if not completely, comprised of organic compounds; so the basic incineration process involves the following oxidation equation:

$$C_xH_yCl_z + O_2 \rightarrow CO_2 + H_2O + HCl + Others \qquad (2\text{-}21)$$

In this reaction, heat energy first volatilizes the organic constituent and then begins to disrupt the intermolecular bonds, causing the molecules to break down (pyrolyze). Oxygen then contacts the organic components of the wastes, and the reaction follows. The completeness of the reaction depends upon the combustion temperature, the reaction time, the gas turbulence, and the availability of oxygen (Shen, 1983).

Numerous incineration processes are commercially available that have been demonstrated to highly effective for the destruction of wastes. The following five technologies in particular comprise the vast majority of the currently operating incineration processes for which data have been developed demonstrating their applicability to the destruction of organic-bearing wastes:

- Liquid injection incinerators.
- Rotary kilns.
- Fixed hearth incinerators.
- Multiple hearth incinerators.
- Fluidized-bed incinerators.

MASS TRANSFER FUNDAMENTALS

VOC emissions from waste treatment sources can enter the atmosphere in two ways: (1) as a result of forced bulk motion on a macroscopic scale (sometimes referred to as convection or advection), and (2) as a result of diffusion on a molecular or turbulent scale. Examples of forced motion include vapor losses during filling of a storage tank, vapor movement in a tank or a landfill cell due to pressure gradients created by changes in atmospheric pressure, and upward convective movement of gas due to biogas production in landfills. VOC emissions resulting from the forced motions do not depend on the volatility of the compound; all molecules simply participate in the macroscopic-scale gas motion.

Diffusion of a VOC from a waste source can be thought of in terms of escape of material through multiple layers presenting varying resistance to mass transfer. For example, as illustrated in Figure 2-1, nonturbulent diffusive transport in a lagoon proceeds through four stages: the bulk liquid, a laminar liquid layer at the liquid surface, a similar laminar air layer, and the atmosphere. The rates of mass transfer (diffusion) through all layers, combined, determine the release rate to the atmosphere. This transfer rate is expressed in terms of the mass transfer coefficient, as will be described later. A compound's volatility, characterized by Henry's law constant as well as by its solubility, partial pressure, and other thermodynamic properties, provides an indication of the quantity of material that will be subjected to the transfer process. Additionally, turbulence in any of the layers can significantly increase the transfer rate (e.g., mixing in a treatment tank) (Sutton, 1953).

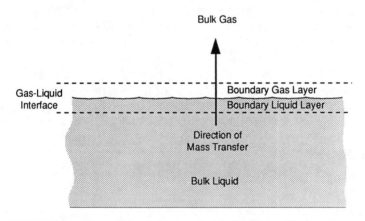

FIGURE 2-1.   Nonturbulent two-layer model of mass transfer for a lagoon.

Generally, transfer rates in one, or perhaps two, of several layers will be so low (due to the high resistance in these layers) that these layers will control the overall atmospheric emission rate. The laminar air or liquid phase for a lagoon (or both for some compounds) will control the overall transfer rate.

Similarly, the volatilization process in landfills can be considered as occurring through diffusion from bulk waste, through a wetted soil region, through a porous region in soil, and into a laminar air layer. However, the porous space in soil dominates overall gaseous flow because diffusion or bulk flow through the void space of the porous soil will control the volatilization rate. For open portions of a landfill, precisely which environmental layer will control the overall release rate will depend on the specific compound of interest and whether, for example, compounds placed initially on the soil surface have seeped deeply into the soil.

All state-of-the art models for emission rate prediction are based on mass transfer principles and fundamental mathematical theories. Whenever the concentration of a chemical or a compound varies between two regions, there is a natural tendency for mass to be transferred across the interface, and to approach equilibrium within the system. Each model is based on the following relationships, which describe diffusive transport across a series of different layers:

- Mass flux = (overall mass transfer coefficient) × (driving force).
- The mass flux equals the net quantity of material transferred across a unit area normal to the surface in a given unit of time (i.e., grams of a chemical transferred across one square centimeter on an air–liquid interface in one second, abbreviated g/cm^2-sec).
- The mass transfer coefficient, for overall layers (K) or for an individual layer (k), is related to the degree of chemical transfer for volatilization.
- The reciprocal of the overall K-value is equal to the sum of the reciprocals of individual k-values for each region. Thus, the overall mass transfer coefficient represents the overall speed of chemical movement, which is based on the sum of the reciprocals of resistance in each region.
- The driving force equals the difference in chemical potential (i.e., chemical concentration) of the compounds of interest on each side of the boundary between two regions.

Several researchers have developed empirical relationships to describe the mass transfer of contaminants from individual regions or phases (i.e., through soil, liquid, and air). Mass transfer correlations have been developed through laboratory experimentation and limited field studies.

Soil Phase Mass Transfer Coefficient

In order to model VOC emission from landfills and land farms, vapor movement within the soil must be accurately defined (Shen, 1986) (Shen, 1984) (Thibodeaux, 1981). The "effective" diffusion coefficient for soil is defined as a function of the volatile component's molecular diffusivity and the physical characteristics of the soil (Farmer et al., 1978).

Ordinary diffusion involves mixing due to the random motion of molecules, affected to a large extent by turbulence and obstruction. With a soil matrix, diffusion of a gas is affected by the size and the arrangement of interconnected voids or pores created by the soil particles. Two factors make diffusion through this medium less than that expressed by the molecular diffusivity: (1) the decreased interfacial area, reduced by the presence of soil particles; and (2) the increased diffusion path, which is a function of soil particle size, shape, and arrangement. Increases in soil moisture also will increase the length of the diffusion path and decrease the dry (air-filled) pore volume available for gaseous diffusion. Thus, mass transfer within soils can be described in terms of an "effective" diffusion coefficient, which is a function of the air-filled porosity, soil particle geometry, and soil moisture content.

The effective diffusion coefficient presented by Farmer was formulated from the theoretical soil hydraulic conductivity studies of Millingan and Quirk (1961), who presented the following correlation for the effective vapor diffusion coefficient:

$$\frac{D_e}{D_o} = \frac{\varepsilon_a^{10/3}}{\varepsilon_T^2} \tag{2-22}$$

where D_e is the effective diffusion coefficient in soil, D_o is the air diffusion coefficient, ε_a is the air-filled porosity, and ε_T is the total porosity.

For a completely dry soil, $\varepsilon_a = \varepsilon_T$, and this expression reduces to the following (Hwang, 1986):

$$\frac{D_e}{D_o} = \varepsilon_T^{4/3} \tag{2-23}$$

Liquid Phase Mass Transfer Coefficient

The transfer of a chemical compound within a liquid medium is identified for two specific cases: (1) diffusion within the liquid phase enhanced by the turbulence created by wind, and (2) diffusion within the liquid phase enhanced by the turbulence of mechanical aeration. Studies have shown that for no-wind situations, thermal agitation has a significant enhancing effect on evaporation (Shen 1982a) (Mackay, Leinonen, 1975) (Mccord, 1981).

Attempts to predict the removal of chemical compounds from water have focused on empirical measurements of volatilization in the laboratory and measurements of stream reaeration rates. Correlations to predict the liquid phase mass transfer coefficient are presented as functions of water flow and wind velocity (i.e., wind-induced flow).

Based a critical review of the existing volatilization data, which included both laboratory experiments and field measurements in lakes, Mackay presented what are considered reasonable values for the liquid phase mass transfer coefficient (K_L) for environmental and laboratory conditions as a function of wind speed (Mackay, 1981). These data for benzene at 20°C are shown in Table 2-9.

Current efforts to identify a liquid phase mass transfer coefficient for environmental applications revolve around field validation of surface impoundment models in general (Liss, Slater, 1974) (Smith, Bomberger, 1982). Improvements in existing correlations can be made by accounting for physical parameters of surface impoundments, including pitch and depth, as it appears from available data that these two parameters are quite influential in K_L determinations. At present, Mackay's "reasonable" values provide a good approximation of liquid phase transfer.

As the concentration of contaminants in soil increases, the volatilization rate will increase proportionately, until the contaminant vapor pressure at the soil–air interface does not increase further. At this point, the soil is considered to have reached the saturation point, at which the soil is saturated with contaminants for volatilization. The degree of saturation of soil with contaminants will influence the volatilization rate. As more contaminants are available in soil for volatilization, the change in concentration of contaminants in soil will be less obvious as volatilization progresses. Soil that is below the saturation point will establish the dynamic concentration profile as the process continues. The concentration profile will determine the diffusional rate of volatilization in addition to emissions

TABLE 2-9.   Liquid phase mass transfer coefficients, K_L, for benzene at 20°C (m/sec).

Wind speed (m/sec)	Environment	Laboratory
2	5×10^{-6}	10×10^{-6}
5	15×10^{-6}	25×10^{-6}
10	35×10^{-6}	65×10^{-6}
15	60×10^{-6}	100×10^{-6}

due to convective flow. The emission rate through changing soil conditions can be estimated by solving appropriate partial differential equations incorporating the fate and transport processes occurring in the soil.

REFERENCES

Cohen, Y., W. Cocchio, and D. Mackay, 1978. Laboratory Studies of Liquid Phase Controlled Volatilization Rates in the Presence of Wind Waves. *Environmental Science; Technology*. Vol. 12, pp. 553–558.

CSDOH, 1975. Hazardous Waste Management—Law, Regulations, and Guidelines For the Handling of Hazardous Waste. California State Department of Health.

Ehrenfeld, J. R., et al. 1986. Controlling Volatile Emissions at Hazardous Waste Sites. Noyes Publication: *Pollution Technology Review,* No. 126, pp. 322–324.

Farmer, W. J., M. S. Yang, and J. Letey, 1978. Land Disposal of Hexachlorobenzene Wastes: Controlling Vapor Movement in Soils. EPA-600/2-80-119.

Federal Register, July 1991. Hazardous Waste TSDFs; Organic Air Emission Standards; Proposed Rule. Vol. 56, No. 140.

Freeman, R. A., Stripping of Hazardous Chemicals from Surface Aerated Waste Treatment Basins. In: APCA/WACF Specialty Conference on Control of Specific Toxic Pollutants. Gainsville, FL. Feb. 13–16, 1979.

Hwang, S. T., 1986. Technical Support Document Mathematical Model Selection Criteria for Performing Exposure Assessments: Airborne Contaminants from Hazardous Waste Facilities. Office of Health and Environmental Assessment, Office of Research and Development, U.S. EPA.

Liss, P. S., and P. G. Slater, 1974. Flux of Gasses across the Air–Sea Surface. *Nature,* No. 247, p. 181.

Lyman, W. L., W. F. Rechl, and D. H. Rosenvlatt, 1982. *Handbook of Chemical Property Estimation Methods.* McGraw-Hill, New York.

Mackay, D., and P. L. Leinonen, 1975. Rate of Evaporation of Low-Solubility Contaminants from Water Bodies to Atmosphere. *Environmental Science and Technology,* Vol. 17(4), p. 211, 1983.

McCord, A. T., 1981. Study of the Emission Rate of Volatile Compounds from Lagoons. *Proceedings* of the Second National Conference of Management of Uncontrolled Hazardous Waste Sites, Washington, D.C.

Millingan, R. J., and J. P. Quirk, 1961. Permeability of Porous Solids. *Trans. Faraday Society,* Vol. 57, pp. 1200–1207.

New York State Department of Environmental Conservation, 1986. New York State Air Guide-1, Guidelines for the Control of Toxic Ambient Air Contaminants.

Owen, M. R., et al., 1964. Some Reaeration Studies in Streams. *International J. Air and Water Pollution,* Vol. 8, p. 496.

Shen, T. T., 1982a. Estimation of Organic Compound Emissions from Waste Lagoons. *J. APCA,* Vol. 32, No. 1, pp. 79–82.

Shen, T. T., 1982b. Air Quality Assessment for Land Disposal of Industrial Wastes. *Environmental Management,* Vol. 6, pp. 297–305.

Shen, T. T., 1983. Hazardous Waste Incineration. A short course manual published by Air Pollution Control Association, Pittsburgh, PA.

Shen, T. T., 1984. Air Pollution Assessment: Toxic Emissions from Hazardous Waste Lagoons and Landfills. *Proceedings* of the International Seminars on Environmental Impact Assessment, University of Aberdeen, Scotland, July 8–21.

Smith, J. H., and D. C. Bomberger, 1982. Prediction of Volatilization Rates of High Volatility Chemicals form Natural Water Bodies. *Environmental Science and Technology,* Vol. 14, No. 11.

Sutton, O. G., 1953. *Micrometeorology.* Krieger Publishing Company, Huntington, NY.

Thibodeaux, L. J., 1981. Estimating the Air Emissions of Chemicals from Hazardous Waste Landfills. *J. Hazardous Materials,* Vol. 4, pp. 235–244.

Shen, T. T., and T. J. Tofflemire. Air Pollution Aspects of Land Disposal of Toxic Wastes. *Environmental Engineering Division Journal.* 106:211–226, 1980.

Shen, T. T., Emission Estimation of Hazardous Organic Compounds from Waste Disposal Sites. Presented at the Air Pollution Control Association Annual Meeting. Montreal, Quebec. June 1980.

Thibodeaux, L. J. Air Stripping of Organics from Wastewater. Proceedings from the Second Annual Conference on Complete Water Use. Chicago, IL, May 4–8, 1978.

U.S. EPA, 1986. Treatment Technology for Solvent Containing Wastes. Technical Resource Document of Hazardous Waste Engineering Research Laboratory, Section 9 Biological Methods, EPA/600/2-86/095, p. 9-1.

Wheast, R. C., Editor, 1971. *The Handbook of Chemistry and Physics.* The Chemical Rubber Company, Cleveland, OH.

3

VOC Emission Sources

VOC emission sources at publicly owned treatment works (POTWs) and RCRA treatment, storage, and disposal facilities (TSDFs) are typically dilute and distributed sources. The majority of VOC emissions come from area sources ranging in size from 10 to 1,000 square meters. Both POTW and TSDF emission sources are similar in size and configuration. The difference lies mainly in the source strength and characterization. TSDF sources normally will be much more concentrated, and more toxic, than POTW sources. This chapter focuses on the emission sources at TSDFs, but the concepts for POTWs are similar, with the POTWs being less concentrated and less toxic.

An EPA national survey (*Federal Register*, 1991) indicated that total nationwide organic emissions from hazardous waste treatment, storage, and disposal facilities (TSDF) at baseline are estimated to be approximately 1.8 million megagrams per year (Mg/yr). These emissions represent approximately 12% of total nationwide, stationary source emissions of organic compounds. The emission estimates presented in Table 3-1 indicate that the major TSDF organic emission sources are tanks, surface impoundments, containers, and waste fixation operations (*Federal Register*, 1991).

The TSDF emission sources described in this chapter include tanks, surface impoundments, containers, waste fixation, land treatment units, landfills, waste piles, hazardous waste incinerators, treatment unit processes vents, and equipment leaks.

Variations in design and operation exist for each of these ten major sources. Thus, the rate of VOC emissions are unit-specific and site-specific. For example, surface impoundments are used to treat, store, and dispose of wastewater that contains hazardous substances. In these scenarios, an impoundment may or may not be aerated, a characteristic that

TABLE 3-1.   Nationwide TSDF organic emissions estimates.

Emission source type	Number of TSDF with source type	Nationwide Organic Emissions (thousands Mg/yr)	
		Current	Baseline
Tanks[1]			
Storage and quiescent treatment	911	800	810
Nonquiescent treatment	291	440	440
Surface impoundments			
Storage and quiescent treatment	270	210	210
Nonquiescent treatment	127	74	74
Containers[2]	1,440	85	85
Waste fixation[3]	158	2	180
Land treatment units	54	73	0[5]
Landfills	90	40	2[4]
Waste piles	57	<1	<1[5]
Hazardous waste incinerators	158	1	1[5]
Treatment unit process vents[6]	450	8	1[5]
TSDF equipment leaks	1,440	26	7[5]
TOTAL		1,760	1,811

1. Estimates do not include generator accumulation tanks.
2. Estimates do not include generator accumulation containers.
3. Waste solidification processes involve the mixing of a waste and a binder in a tank, surface impoundment, container, or other type of hazardous waste management unit.
4. Baseline estimate assumes waste will be treated to remove or destroy organics prior to placement in the unit to comply with land disposal restrictions.
5. Organic emissions are regulated by existing RCRA standards.
6. Distillation, fractionation, evaporation, solvent extraction, air stripping, and steam stripping waste treatment processes are used.

can significantly enhance potential emission rates. Similarly, a landfill may exist in three distinct operational phases: (1) open with the waste exposed to the atmosphere, (2) closed with a temporary cover, or (3) closed with a final cap. The potential VOC emissions for a landfill can be considerably different, depending upon the distribution of total landfilled surface area between each of these phases and the duration of each phase. The relative emission rate potential from the two covered phases depends primarily on the depths of soil cover and types of soil used (Hwang, 1986).

Typical emission rates from various sources by pollutant class have been compiled by EPA as follows (U.S. EPA, 1987):

- Uncontrolled sources, in Table 3-2.
- Remediation sources, in Table 3-3.
- Controlled sources, in Table 3-4.

TABLE 3-2. Typical emission rates by pollutant class: uncontrolled sources.

Source	Pollutant class	Emission rates (kg/day, unless otherwise noted)
Landfills	Volatile and semivolatile organics	4.18×10^{-5}–1.06×10^{-3} kg/m^2/day
	Particulates	Not available
Lagoons	Volatile and semivolatile organics	6.19×10^{-5} kg/m^2/day
	Particulates	Not significant
Contaminated soil surfaces		
Land treatment	Volatile and semivolatile organics	Not available
	Particulates	Not available
Waste piles	Volatile and semivolatile organics	Not available
	Particulates	1.62×10^{-5}–6.25×10^{-5} kg/m^2/day
Aboveground containers		
Tanks	Volatile and semivolatile organics	11.54
	Particulates	Not significant
Container storage areas	Volatile and semivolatile organics	0.066
	Particulates	Not significant

Source: U.S. EPA, 1987.

TABLE 3-3. Typical emission rates by pollutant class: remediation sources.

Source	Pollutant class	Emission rates (kg/day, unless otherwise noted)
Soil handling	Volatile and semivolatile organics	Not available
	Particulates	27.08 – 168.2
Air strippers	Volatile and semivolatile organics	0.05 – 2.5
	Particulates	Not significant
Incinerators*	Volatile and semivolatile organics	$3.82 \times 10^{-7} - 8.1 \times 10^{-3}$
	Particulates	1.5 – 69
	NO_x	$1.14 \times 10^{-7} - 4.57 \times 10^{-5}$
	HF	$9.92 \times 10^{-8} - 9.92 \times 10^{-7}$
	HCl	$4.52 \times 10^{-7} - 4.52 \times 10^{-5}$
	SO_2	$1.59 \times 10^{-7} - 1.90 \times 10^{-4}$
In situ venting	Volatile and semivolatile organics (uncontrolled emissions)	1–110 kg/day per recovery well
	Volatile and semivolatile organics (uncontrolled emissions)	0.01–5.5 kg/day per recovery well
Solidification/stabilization	Volatile and semivolatile organics	Not available
	Particulates	124–164

* Assumes 96% efficiency for pollution control device.

Source: U.S. EPA, 1987.

TABLE 3-4. Typical emission rates by pollutant class: controlled sources.

Source	Pollutant class	Emission rates (kg/day, unless otherwise noted)
Landfills	Volatile and semivolatile organics	1.30×10^{-5}–2.16×10^{-4} kg/m^2/day
	Particulates	Not available
Lagoons	Volatile and semivolatile organics	1.30×10^{-5}–9.07×10^{-4} kg/m^2/day
	Particulates	Not significant
Contaminated soil surfaces		
Land treatment	Volatile and semivolatile organics	8.78×10^{-4}–0.014 kg/m^2/day
	Particulates	Not available
Waste piles	Volatile and semivolatile organics	Not available
	Particulates	1.95×10^{-4}–7.5×10^{-4} kg/m^2/day
Aboveground containers		
Tanks	Volatile and semivolatile organics	11.54
	Particulates	Not significant
Container storage areas	Volatile and semivolatile organics	0.066
	Particulates	Not significant

Source: U.S. EPA, 1987.

40

TANKS

Tanks are used at TSDFs for storage and for treatment of waste. Most TSDF storage tanks presently are either open-top or covered and vented to the atmosphere. A few storage tanks are vented to a control device. Emissions from tanks occur as a result of evaporation at the liquid surface of the waste. For open tanks, the evaporated organics are dispersed into the atmosphere by diffusion, wind, or displacement during tank filling. Emissions from treatment tanks that use aeration, agitation, or mixing operations tend to be higher than those from storage tanks. However, emissions from tanks used for treatment processes such as clarification, sedimentation, or neutralization where no mechanical mixing is involved and waste remains in a quiescent state are similar to emissions for storage tanks.

VOC emissions from storage tanks are a function of several factors, including (1) physical and chemical characteristics of the liquids, (2) temperature level and diurnal fluctuations, (3) tank design, (4) tank condition, and (5) operational characteristics, especially turnover frequency. Tanks may be classified into five basic types, listed in increasing order of emissions potential as follows:

1. Open tank.
2. Fixed roof.
3. Internal and external floating roof.
4. Variable vapor space.
5. Pressure tank.

A typical fixed-roof tank is shown in Figure 3-1. VOC emissions from fixed-roof tanks result from breathing losses and working losses. Breathing loss is defined as vapor expulsion due to vapor expansion and contraction from changes in tank temperature and ambient barometric pressure. The combined loss from periodic filling and emptying is called the working loss.

An internal floating-roof storage tank has a permanently affixed roof and a cover inside the tank that floats on the liquid surface (contact), or that rests on pontoons several inches above the liquid surface (noncontact). Figures 3-2 and 3-3 illustrate the contact and noncontact designs of internal floating-roof tanks. An external floating-roof tank is shown as Figure 3-4. Both tanks have the same sources of emissions, standing storage and working losses.

Tanks comprise the largest TSDF organic emission source. As a group, they are estimated to emit approximately 756,000 Mg/yr nationwide, of

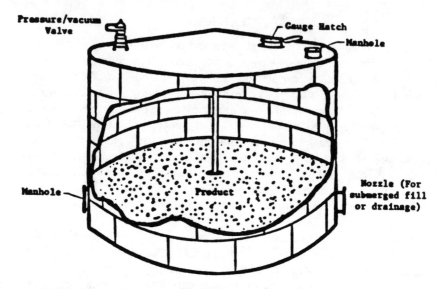

FIGURE 3-1.   Typical fixed-roof storage tank.   (*Source:* U.S. EPA, 1981)

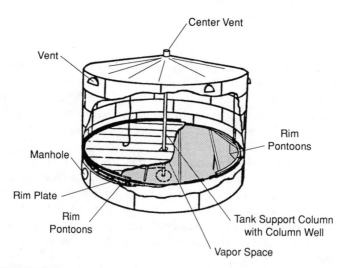

FIGURE 3-2.   Contact internal floating roof.   (*Source:* U.S. EPA, 1981)

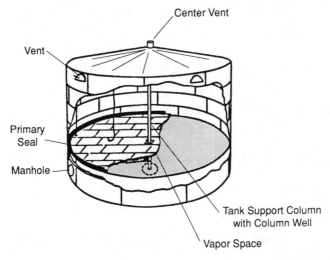

FIGURE 3-3.   Noncontact internal floating roof.   (*Source:* U.S. EPA, 1981)

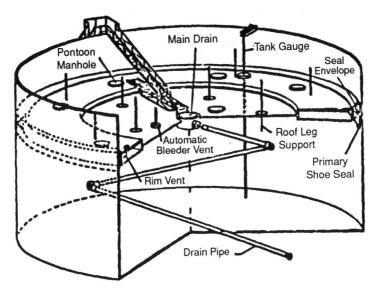

FIGURE 3-4.   Typical external floating-roof storage tank.   (*Source:* U.S. EPA, 1981)

which 440,000 Mg/yr are from tanks managing nonquiescent wastes (*Federal Register*, 1991).

SURFACE IMPOUNDMENTS

A surface impoundment is a natural topographic depression, man-made excavation, or diked area formed primarily of earthen materials designed to hold an accumulation of liquid wastes, or wastes containing some liquids.

Surface impoundments may be operated individually or may be interconnected with other impoundments so that the wastewater flow moves in series or in parallel fashion. Treatment impoundments may employ aerators to increase air stripping of volatile constituents in the wastewater or to enhance biological activity. Storage impoundments may be discharged continuously or periodically, whereas disposal impoundments are designed to lose the fluids by evaporation or infiltration into the soil.

The primary source of VOC emissions from surface impoundments or lagoons is emissions from the free liquid surface. Uncontrolled sites are not likely to have mechanisms in place (e.g., temporary covers) to control emissions from the liquid surface. VOC emissions occur through evaporation, and generation of vapors occurs through wave action. Mechanically aerated lagoons have a greater potential for emissions than quiescent lagoons. The degree of emissions is affected by the volatility of the liquid in the impoundment, and by environmental factors such as temperature, atmospheric pressure, and wind speed.

Diffusion of volatile organic compounds from a lagoon can be thought of in terms of escape of material through layers presenting varying resistance to mass transfer. Nonturbulent diffusive transport in a lagoon proceeds through four stages: the bulk liquid, a laminar liquid layer at the liquid surface, a similar air layer, and, finally, the atmosphere.

Surface impoundments also are a large source of TSDF emissions, releasing them directly to the atmosphere from the exposed waste surface. Organic emissions from storage and quiescent treatment surface impoundments are estimated to be 210,000 Mg/yr nationwide (*Federal Register*, 1991).

CONTAINERS

Containers include drums, tank trucks, railroad tank cars, and dumpsters. Although existing RCRA regulations requiring containers to be closed during storage help reduce VOC emissions, organic emissions will result from gaps between the container lip and the cover unless a tight-fitting cover is used.

Emissions during container loading operations occur when liquid or sludge wastes are poured into a container, displacing an equal volume of air that is saturated or nearly saturated with the organic from inside the container to the ambient air. Organic emissions associated with the transfer and storage of waste in containers are estimated to be 85,000 Mg/yr (*Federal Register*, 1991).

WASTE FIXATION

Certain liquid, slurry, and sludge hazardous wastes are now treated at TSDFs using a waste fixation process (also referred to as waste solidification or stabilization) so that the waste can be placed in a hazardous waste landfill. It is a chemical process used to react the free water in the waste with a binder (such as cement kiln or lime kiln dust) to form a solid material that immobilizes specific metal and organic contaminants in the waste.

Waste fixation involves making the waste with the binder, dumping the waste into an open-tank, surface impoundment, waste pile, or dumpster, and adding the binder, using a backhoe or other construction machinery. Organic emissions from waste fixation occur when organics in the waste volatilize and are released during mixing and curing. Emissions from waste fixation operations are estimated at 2,000 Mg/yr. These emissions are expected to increase significantly above the current level because it is assumed that the TSDF industry will respond to land disposal regulations by using waste fixation to convert dilute aqueous liquids, aqueous sludges/slurries, and high-solids-content waste mixtures into solid materials that can be placed in a landfill (*Federal Register*, 1991).

LAND TREATMENT UNITS

Land treatment involves first treating the waste by spreading it on top of or injecting it into soil, and then tilling the soil to allow soil bacteria to decompose the organic material and to fix the metals in the soil matrix. Organic emissions are generated during application, tilling, and decomposing, both from direct volatilization of organics that are land-treated and from volatile organics that are formed during the decomposition of heavy organics. If a dewatering device is used, emissions also may occur from this device. However, the major emission source in the land treatment operation itself is the soil surface. Emissions from land treatment operations are estimated at 73,000 Mg/yr (*Federal Register*, 1991).

VOC emissions from land treatment are expected to be reduced to a minimum because of the following land disposal regulations: (1) all wastes currently land-treated with the exception of high-solids-content waste mixtures will instead be incinerated, and (2) the high-solids-content waste mixtures will be treated by waste fixation and then landfill.

LANDFILLS

Landfill design and operation are generally determined by the local topography, depth to groundwater, and availability of natural clay formations that act as liners. Figure 3-5 through 3-7 illustrate three landfill construc-

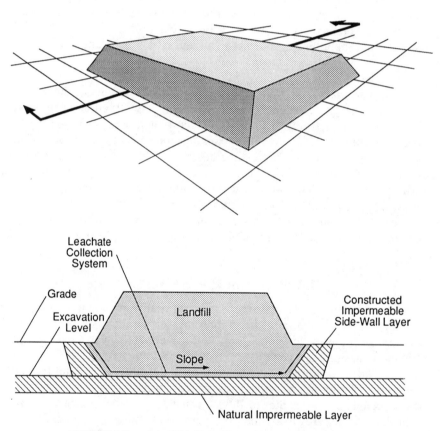

FIGURE 3-5.   Landfill built below original grade in flat terrain.

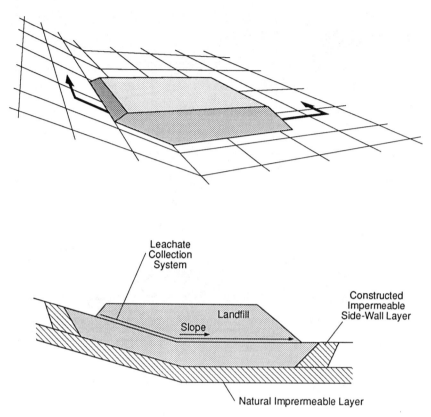

FIGURE 3-6.   Landfill built on original grade in sloped terrain.

tion options that maximize the topographic configurations while minimizing excavation and grading. All three options benefit from natural impermeable strata. When conditions do not allow for a natural liner, an artificial one such as a thermoplastic membrane must be used.

In addition to site topography, the method of filling is dependent upon the waste characteristics. Dry and immediately workable waste may be spread in horizontal layers 6 inches to 2 feet thick with successive layering occurring to heights of 10 to 20 feet. These layers commonly are referred to as lifts. Figure 3-8 shows a cross section of this type of landfill development. Wet waste that is not immediately workable may be mixed with dry, compatible waste or soil before disposal. Containerized wastes disposed of in such a fashion require careful placement and covering. Void spaces between the containers must be filled to prevent uneven settling of the cover and premature rupture of the containers.

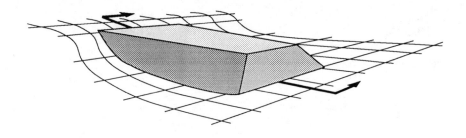

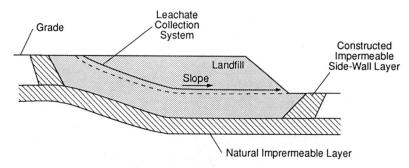

FIGURE 3-7.   Landfill in valley that forms three sides of the containment basin.

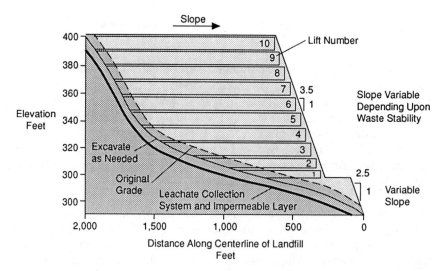

FIGURE 3-8.   Typical section through centerline of valley landfill, showing lift details.

Several methods of landfill construction exist, including the trench, area, and ramp methods. Each method uses different techniques for waste placement, compaction, and cover. However, many landfills have been accepting waste for decades without adequate records of waste placement techniques or waste characteristics, and with few technological controls, such as liners or cover systems, that would prevent escape of waste or waste constituents to the environment. For this reason, air emissions from uncontrolled landfills are primarily area source emissions that occur through a variety of mechanisms.

There are two primary area sources of gaseous emissions from land-fills: (1) lateral and vertical diffusion of volatile organic compounds through the overburden or landfill cover, and (2) exposure of contaminated soils and waste through water and wind erosion of cover material with subsequent evaporation and/or sublimation of exposed liquid or solids. The rate of volatile emissions through the first mechanism, diffusion through the landfill overburden or cover, is proportional to the volatility and the areal extent of the emission source. If the contaminant source is highly volatile (expressed as a high vapor pressure or a high Henry's law constant), volatile emissions will occur at a high rate. Likewise, if there is widespread soil or groundwater contamination, diffusion of volatile organics through the overburden will occur more rapidly than if the contaminant source is confined to a smaller area (U.S. EPA, 1987). The second non-point source of gaseous emissions is dependent on both the construction and the maintenance of the landfill cover system, and on factors that influence erosion such as rainfall rates and wind patterns.

The most significant point source of VOC emissions from landfills is active gas venting system emissions. Active gas venting systems employ either vacuum or positive pressure pumping to extract gases from landfill soils. The extent of emissions from this source depends on the presence and/or efficiency of the emission control device at the gas collection source.

Emissions can occur from both active and closed landfill facilities. In an active landfill, whether open or covered with earth, the landfill surface is the major emission point. Other activities generating emissions at an active site include waste transport, unloading, and spreading. Emissions from active landfills are estimated to be 40,000 Mg/yr. Although the amount of waste landfilled after implementation of landfill regulations is expected to increase over current levels because of increased waste fixation, emissions are expected to be substantially reduced because of the assumptions that: (1) land disposal regulations will require that the fixated wastes contain no free organics, and (2) all organic lipid and organic sludge/slurry wastes currently placed in landfills will instead be incinerated in response to the land disposal regulations. Emissions from closed landfills are difficult to estimate because of the need for information related to the waste types and quantities as well as when the waste was buried at the site. Therefore, emissions from closed landfills could not be estimated as of mid-1991 (*Federal Register*, 1991).

WASTE PILES

A waste pile is used for the short-term storage of wastes, and organic emissions can be released by volatilization from the waste pile surface. Emissions from TSDF waste piles are estimated to be 130 Mg/yr. There are no estimates of emissions from waste piles at industrial sites or uncontrolled hazardous waste sites. It is assumed that all organic liquid and organic sludge/slurry wastes currently placed in waste piles ultimately will be incinerated in response to land disposal regulations (*Federal Register*, 1991).

HAZARDOUS WASTE INCINERATORS

Organic emissions are released from the exhaust stacks of hazardous waste incinerators as well as boilers and industrial furnaces used to burn hazardous waste. Emissions from hazardous waste incinerators are estimated to be 880 Mg/yr. It is assumed that increased quantities of waste will be incinerated in response to land disposal regulations; so VOC emissions from incineration are expected to increase to a level of over 1,000 Mg/yr (*Federal Register*, 1991). VOC emissions from hazardous waste incinerators are regulated by RCRA standards in 40 CFR 264 Subpart O.

TREATMENT UNIT PROCESS VENTS

Organic emissions are released from the process vents of distillation, fractionation, evaporation, solvent extraction, air stripping, and steam stripping units used to treat hazardous wastes containing volatile organics. Emissions from these TSDF sources are estimated to be 8,100 Mg/yr. VOC emission standards for process vents (Subpart AA in 40 CFR Parts 264 and 265) are in effect and are expected to reduce process vent emissions to less than 1,000 Mg/yr (*Federal Register*, 1991).

TSDF EQUIPMENT LEAKS

Emissions from equipment leaks occur when waste leaks from seals, gaskets, sampling connections, or other openings in waste handling processes. Equipment leak emissions from TSDF handling waste having an organic content of 10% or more are estimated at 26,200 Mg/yr (*Federal Register*, 1991). Air emission standards for equipment leaks (Subpart BB in 40 CFR Parts 264 and 265) are in effect and are expected to reduce these VOC emissions to an insignificant amount.

REFERENCES

Federal Register, July 22, 1991. Hazardous Waste TSDFs; Organic Air Emission Standards; Proposed Rule. Vol. 56, No. 140.

Federal Register, Feb. 5, 1981. Hazardous Waste Management System; Standards Applicable to Owners and Operators of TSDFs; and Permit Program. Vol. 46, No. 24.

Hwang, S. T., 1986. Technical Support Document on Mathematical Model Selection Criteria for Performing Exposure Assessments: Airborne Contaminants from Hazardous Waste Facilities. EPA Office of Health and Environmental Assessment, Washington, D.C.

U.S. EPA, 1987. Hazardous Waste Treatment, Storage, and Disposal Facilities— Air Emission Models Draft Document. QAQPS/RTP.

4

Regulations

The growing concern over possible links between exposure to hazardous pollutants and human cancers has provided the impetus for regulatory control of the waste management facilities that produce hazardous pollutants. The ultimate goal is to assure that all waste management facilities handle, treat, and dispose of waste properly.

The legal structures designed to control hazardous pollutants from waste management facilities usually represent a compromise between the public health and welfare on the one hand and technical, economic, and political factors on the other. The manner in which this compromise is achieved largely depends on the situation existing in each jurisdiction or country. This chapter briefly highlights existing and currently proposed air emission laws, regulations, and standards associated with VOC emissions from publicly owned treatment works (POTWs) and RCRA waste treatment, storage, and disposal facilities (TSDFs).

THE RESOURCE CONSERVATION AND RECOVERY ACT (RCRA)

RCRA was enacted in 1976 as an amendment to the Solid Waste Disposal Act (SWDA). The primary objectives of RCRA are to protect human health and the environment and to conserve valuable material and energy resources. The most important aspect of RCRA is its establishment of "cradle-to-grave" management and tracking of hazardous waste, from generator to transporter to treatment, storage, and disposal. Other aspects of RCRA include the development of solid waste management plans; prohibition of open dumping; encouragement of recycling, reuse, and treatment of hazardous wastes; establishment of guidelines for solid waste management; and promotion of beneficial solid waste management, resource recovery, and resource conservation systems. Additionally, under corrective action provisions, RCRA also regulates cleanup of contamination, much as the Comprehensive Environmental Response, Compensation, and Liability Act (CERCLA or Superfund) does. However, RCRA concentrates on active, regulated facilities, whereas CERCLA focuses on inactive or uncontrolled sites.

Under Subtitle C of RCRA as amended, EPA is required to issue regulations setting forth a complete "cradle-to-grave" system for the management of hazardous waste. EPA has elected to issue these regulations in phases. On February 26, 1990, EPA promulgated standards for generators and transporters of hazardous wastes in 40 CFR Parts 262 and 263. These standards were republished with technical amendments on May 19, 1990. On that date, EPA promulgated several regulations: a general regulation relating to the several regulations (Part 260); a regulation identifying hazardous waste (Part 261); regulations governing the issuance of permits and the authorization of states to implement a hazardous waste program (Parts 122–124); interim status standards applicable to owners and operators of "existing" hazardous waste treatment, storage, and disposal facilities (Part 265); and administrative, nontechnical standards to be used in issuing permits to owners and operators of treatment, storage, and disposal facilities (Part 264).

Under Sections 3002 and 3004 of RCRA of 1976 as amended by the Hazardous and Solid Waste Act (HSWA) of 1984, Section 3004(n) of RCRA directs EPA to promulgate regulations for the monitoring and the control of air emissions from hazardous waste treatment, storage, and disposal facilities, including open tanks, surface impoundments, and landfills to protect human health and the environment. However, because of the nationwide diversity and complexity of TSDFs, it is a very difficult task to characterize TSDF emission sources, emission quantities, and potential emissions controls. An extensive effort is required for one fully to understand which TSDF emission sources need to be regulated and how best to apply emission controls to those sources.

EPA decided to implement RCRA Section 3004(n) by using a phased approach so that standards could be implemented for certain TSDF emission sources. For the first phase of EPA's program to regulate air emissions under RCRA Section 3004(n), EPA developed standards for certain hazardous waste treatment processes early to coincide with the regulations under RCRA Section(m) restricting the land disposal of untreated hazardous wastes. These land disposal restrictions established standards that require certain hazardous waste to be treated to reduce specific hazardous waste properties (e.g., concentration of individual toxic constituents) before the waste can be placed in a land disposal unit. The first phase has been completed with standards developed to reduce organic emissions vented from the treatment of hazardous wastes by distillation, fractionation, thin-film evaporation, solvent extraction, steam stripping, and air stripping, as well as from leaks in certain piping and equipment used for hazardous waste management processes.

The second phase is intended to regulate organic emissions from TSDF tanks, surface impoundments, containers, and certain miscellaneous units. In both the first and the second phases, standards are developed that control organic emissions as a class rather than pollutant by pollutant. EPA claims that the regulation of organics as a class is relatively straightforward because it can be accomplished by a single standard, whereas the control of individual toxic pollutants will require multiple standards for which EPA has not yet completed sufficient analysis.

Under the third phase, EPA may develop additional standards applicable to sources regulated in the process vent and equipment leak rule, and to sources covered in Phase II. EPA recognizes that the potential remains for high risk at some TSDFs because of individual chemical constituents or other physical characteristics of the facilities, even after the substantial emission reductions achieved through Phase I and Phase II controls. For this reason, EPA needs to determine the need for standards for the control of emissions of specific toxic waste constituents from all TSDF sources, which may continue to pose a high health risk after the standards for VOCs are implemented.

The Subpart AA standards in 40 CFR Parts 264 and 265 require owners or operators of TSDFs that use the affected waste treatment processes either to: (a) reduce total organic emissions from all affected vents at the facility to less than 1.4 kg/hr (3 lb/hr) and 2,800 kg/yr (3.1 tons/yr), or (b) install and operate a control device(s) that reduces total organic emissions from all affected vents at the facility by 95% by weight (CFR, 1990; *Federal Register*, 1991).

The Subpart BB standards control emissions due to leaks associated with certain types of TSDF process equipment. These standards require implementation of a leak detection and repair program for pumps and valves, and installation and operation of certain equipment on compressors, pressure-relief devices, sampling connection systems, open-ended valves of lines, flanges or other connectors, and associated air emission control devices. The requirements apply to TSDF where the equipment specified above contains or contacts hazardous waste containing organic concentrations of 10% or more by weight.

The proposed Subpart CC of 40 CFR Parts 264 and 265 (*Federal Register*, 1991) adds requirements for owners and operators of hazardous waste treatment and disposal facilities to the RCRA Subtitle C permitting requirements to install and operate organic emission controls on certain tanks, surface impoundments, and containers. The proposed rule adds two new test methods to both 40 CFR Part 60 Appendix A, "Standards of Performance for New Stationary Sources Reference Methods," and EPA Publication No. SW-846, "Test Methods for Evaluating Solid Waste, Physical/Chemical Methods," which is used for determining the VOC content and vapor phase organic concentration in waste samples. The proposed rule specifies the permit terms and provisions for a miscellaneous unit being permitted, including the appropriate emission control requirements for Subparts AA, BB, and CC. The rule also requires owners and operators using carbon absorption systems to comply with the standards to certify that the spent carbon removed from the system is destined either for proper regeneration or for incineration that minimizes the release of organics to the atmosphere.

Standards proposed by EPA on July 22, 1991 require that specific organic emission controls be installed and operated on tanks, surface impoundments, and containers into which is placed hazardous waste with a volatile organic concentration equal to or greater than 500 ppm by weight (ppmw). If, during the course of treating a waste, the organic concentration of the waste decreases below 500 ppmw, emission controls would not be required on the subsequent downstream tanks, surface impoundments, and containers that manage this waste. EPA encourages owners and operators to reduce the volatile organic concentration for a specific waste to a level less than 500 ppmw through pollution prevention adjustments and other engineering techniques.

For the third phase, EPA may issue regulations to address the risk remaining after promulgation of the first two phases. EPA has begun an effort to update and improve the data base used for analyzing the human health and environmental impacts resulting from TSDF air emissions. If regulations are necessary in the third phase, EPA will likely impose controls on individual toxic pollutants.

EPA already has developed RCRA standards to control organic emissions from certain hazardous waste treatment processes. Air emissions from hazardous waste incinerators are regulated by 40 CFR 264 Subpart O. Standards for hazardous waste incinerators limit emissions of organics, particulate matter, and hydrogen chloride. Organic emissions are controlled by requiring a hazardous waste incinerator to achieve a destruction and removal efficiency of 99.99% for each principal organic hazardous pollutant designated for each waste feed. Air emissions from other types of noncombustion treatment processes are controlled by the air standards for TSDF treatment unit process vents and equipment leaks (Subparts AA and BB in 40 CFR 264 and 265).

Standards Applicable to All TSDFs

The following standards apply to all TSDFs:

- RCRA Section 3000 notification to EPA.
- Part A permit applications to EPA.
- Facility management plan: waste analysis, security, inspections, maintenance, training, and requirements for ignitable, reactive, and incompatible waste.
- Location of waste management units.

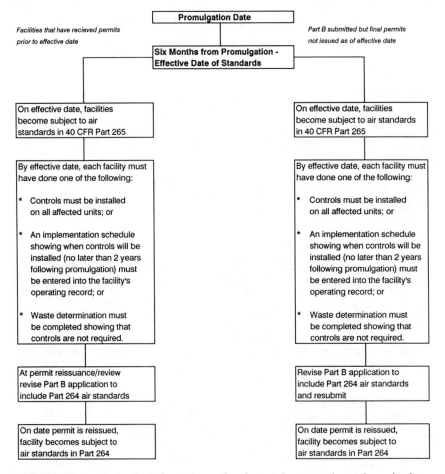

FIGURE 4-1.   Air standards for tanks, surface impoundments, and containers: implementation schedule for existing TSDFs with permits or in interim status.

- Preparedness for and prevention of emergencies and releases.
- Written contingency plan and emergency procedure.
- Written operating records, manifest records, and biennial reports of facility activities.
- Groundwater protection and monitoring for land disposal facilities.
- Correction action.
- Closure plan and post-closure care and use.
- Financial information and guarantees regarding closure, post-closure, accidents, and bankruptcy. (ENSR, 1990)

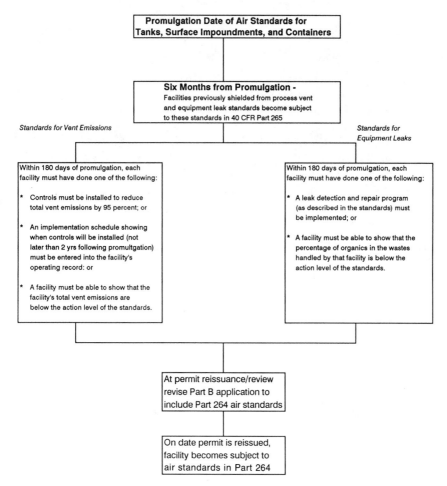

FIGURE 4-2.   Air standards for process vents and equipment leaks: implementation schedule for existing facilities with permits as of (1991).

Air Standards for Tanks, Surface
Impoundments and Containers
An implementation schedule for existing TSDFs with permits or in interim status is presented in Figure 4-1.

Air Standards for Process Vents
and Equipment Leaks
An implementation schedule for existing facilities with permits is presented in Figure 4-2 (*Federal Register*, 1991).

THE COMPREHENSIVE ENVIRONMENTAL RESPONSE, COMPENSATION, AND LIABILITY ACT (CERCLA)

CERCLA is a program intended to identify sites where hazardous substances have been or might have been released into the environment and to ensure that they are cleaned up. It is primarily concerned with abandoned sites. CERCLA of 1990 as amended by the Superfund Amendments and Reauthorization Act of 1986 (SARA) authorizes EPA to undertake removal and remedial actions to clean up hazardous substance releases. Remedial program managers must assess the potential for air emissions and air quality impacts caused by Superfund sites prior to and during cleanup. CERCLA and SARA mandate the characterization of all contaminant migration pathways from the waste to the environment and of the resulting environmental impacts. A remedial investigation must provide data on air emissions from the site in the undisturbed and disturbed states (CERCLA, 1990; SARA, 1986).

Removal actions typically are short-term or temporary measures taken to minimize exposure or danger to human health and the environment from the release of a hazardous pollutant. EPA promulgated clean standards, standards of control, and other substantive environmental protection requirements, criteria, or limitations that specifically address a hazardous substance, pollutant, remedial action, location, or other circumstance of a CERCLA site.

The proposed organic emission control requirements apply to on-site remedial and removal actions that use tanks, surface impoundments, and containers to manage substances identified or listed under RCRA as hazardous waste and containing more than 500 ppmw of volatile organics. CERCLA wastes that are defined as hazardous under RCRA, contain more than 500 ppmw of volatile organics, and are shipped off-site for management in tanks, surface impoundments, and containers, are subject to the proposed standards like any similar RCRA hazardous waste (CER-CLA, 1990).

RCRA/CERCLA Interface

The goal of RCRA is to avoid creating new Superfund sites by regulating hazardous waste management units and requiring corrective action at active hazardous waste TSDFs. In contrast, the major concern of CER-CLA is cleanup of hazardous substance releases at uncontrolled or abandoned hazardous waste sites. The triggering mechanism for CERCLA is a release, or threat of release, of hazardous substances to the environment. However, RCRA corrective action provisions and CERCLA response actions are fast becoming closely aligned. Many Superfund remedial actions are subject to RCRA technical standards (ENSR, 1990).

The Superfund Amendments and Reauthorization Act (SARA) of 1986

SARA is a five-year extension and expansion of CERCLA. It significantly expanded the scope and funding of the Superfund program, added structure to the program including specific deadlines for the more important Superfund activities as well as remedial action tied closely to the administrative record, and encouraged much more public and state involvement in the Superfund process (SARA, 1986).

THE CLEAN AIR ACT (CAA)

The Clean Air Act (CAA) is the law that authorizes regulations governing releases of airborne contaminants from stationary and nonstationary sources. The regulations include National Ambient Air Quality Standards for specific pollutants. Although the Clean Air Act of 1977 brought about significant improvements in air quality in the United States, the urban air pollution problems of ozone, carbon monoxide, and particulate matter (PM-10) persist. Currently, over 100 million American lives in cities that are out of attainment with the public health standards for ozone.

The CAA Amendments of 1990 created a new, balanced strategy for the United States to attack the problem of urban smog derived from high ozone concentration. For the pollutant ozone, the new law established nonattainment area classifications ranked according to the severity of the area's air pollution problem. Ozone nonattainment areas are classified into one of five categories: marginal (0.121 ppm up to 0.138 ppm), moderate (0.138 ppm up to 0.160 ppm), serious (0.160 ppm up to 0.180 ppm), severe (0.180 ppm up to 0.280), and extreme (0.280 ppm and above), based upon the degree to which they exceed the ozone standard. EPA puts each nonattainment area into one of these categories, thus triggering varying requirements that the area must comply with in order to meet the ozone standard (CAAA, 1990).

Control Measures

Nonattainment areas will have to implement different control measures, depending upon their classification (USEPA, 1991). Marginal areas, for example, come closest to meeting the standard. They will be required to conduct an inventory of their ozone-causing emissions such as volatile organic compounds and to institute a permit program. Nonattainment areas with more serious air quality problems must implement various control measures. The worse the air quality is, the more controls areas they will have to implement.

The CAA Amendments of 1990 require that each state with one or more ozone nonattainment areas impose control requirements on VOCs. These control requirements must be sufficient to allow the nonattainment areas to comply with the ambient standard on an aggressive schedule. Many TSDF facilities located in ozone nonattainment areas that previously were considered minor sources of VOCs thus are subject to new controls.

Operating Program

The CAA amendments of 1990 introduced an operating program modeled after a similar program under the Federal National Pollution Elimination Discharge System (NPDES) law. The purpose of the operating permits program is to ensure compliance with all applicable requirements of the CAA and to enhance EPA's ability to enforce the Act. Air pollution sources subject to the program must obtain an operating permit, states must develop and implement the program, and EPA must issue permit program regulations, review each state's proposed program, and oversee the state's effort to implement any approved program. EPA also must develop and implement a federal permit program when a state fails to adopt and implement its own program (U.S. EPA, 1991).

This program, in many ways the most important procedural reform contained in the new law, will greatly strengthen enforcement of the Clean Air Act. First, adding such a program updates the CAA, making it more consistent with other environmental statutes. The Clean Water Act and RCRA all require permits, including those for waste treatment and disposal facilities.

Hazardous Air Pollutants

Title III, Hazardous Air Pollutants, of the CAA Amendments lists 189 chemicals to be regulated and includes a procedure for the EPA to add and delete chemicals from the list. Using this list of chemicals, EPA will publish a list of major point and area sources categories for which emission standards will be developed, and then will publish a schedule establishing a date for the promulgation of these standards. A major source generally is defined as a stationary source located within a contiguous area that emits or has the potential to emit 10 or more tons/yr of any hazardous air pollutants, or 25 or more tons/yr of any combination of hazardous air pollutants (CAAA, 1990).

For each listed source category, EPA will issue standards requiring the maximum degree of emissions reduction that has been demonstrated to be achievable, commonly referred to as maximum achievable control technology (MACT) standards. The primary consideration in establishing these standards must be demonstrated technology. Other considerations that may play some role in standard selection include: costs, non-air-quality health and environmental impacts, and energy requirements. For area sources, EPA may elect to promulgate standards that provide for the use of generally available control technologies of management practices (GACT).

Efforts to achieve early environmental benefits are encouraged in Title III. For example, industries are encouraged to use the provisions that allow an alternative compliance date in exchange for the implementation of an early emission reduction program. Effective use of these provisions will allow industry flexibility in achieving emission reductions and will result in early environmental benefits.

The standards developed under Title III to control hazardous air pollutants will be enforced under the operating permit program required under Title V. Several questions associated with developing emission standards include:

• What is the definition of "source" as it applies to the various provisions of Title III?
• What factors should be considered in differentiating between different types and classes of sources in setting MACT/GACT standards?
• When should GACT and MACT be used for area sources?

- How should guidance be developed on how to use the early emission reduction provisions effectively in order to secure early emission reductions in air toxic emissions?
- How high or low should the hurdle be for granting petitions to add or delete pollutants from the list of hazardous air pollutants or to remove a listed category?

Section 129 of Title III includes provisions for a comprehensive regulatory program for solid waste incinerators. In January 1991, EPA promulgated standards for large-capacity (>250 tons/day) municipal waste incinerators for most pollutants. Regulations for lead, mercury, and cadmium emissions from these incinerators are being promulgated. Standards for small-capacity (<250 tons/day) incinerators were to be promulgated by November 1992. The EPA efforts also will emphasize the development of regulations for medical waste incinerators, commercial and industrial waste incinerators, and all other waste incinerators (CAAA, 1990; STAPPA/ALAPCO, 1990).

Title III also includes provisions to prevent accidental releases of hazardous air pollutants. Implementation of the accidental release provisions will be the responsibility of EPA's Chemical Emergency Preparedness and Prevention Office within the Office of Solid Waste and Emergency Response. By the end of 1992, EPA was to promulgate a list of at least 100 chemicals that, if accidentally released, could seriously damage human health or the environment. Threshold quantities must be established for these pollutants, taking into consideration toxicity, reactivity, volatility, dispersibility, combustibility, and flammability. An overview of Title III's basic requirements is given in Figure 4-3.

Accidental Release

The Act authorizes EPA to promulgate accident prevention regulations. EPA must list at least 100 extremely hazardous air pollutants (16 are listed in the Act) along with threshold amounts. EPA must establish regulations calling for detection and control of accidental releases.

Owners/operators of industrial facilities including waste treatment, storage, and disposal facilities that handle these extremely hazardous substances must prepare risk management plans to identify and prevent potential accidental releases. The information must be made available to the public.

Monitoring

Owners/operators must monitor and report the results of monitoring of (1) emissions into the air at the point at which pollutants are limited, (2) the

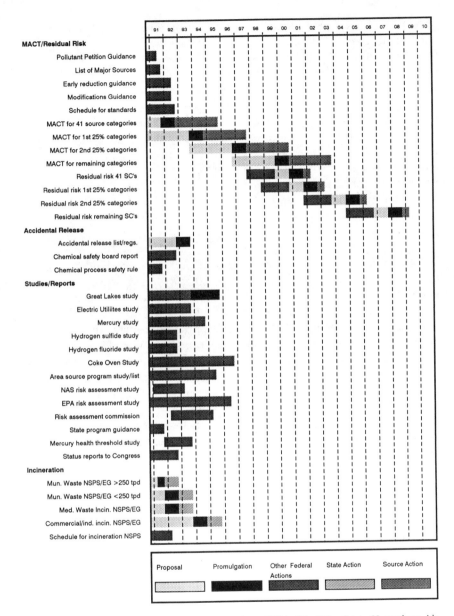

FIGURE 4-3.   Schedule for the implementation of Title III of the CAA: Hazardous Air Pollutants.

operation of the waste incinerator, and (3) the operation of the control equipment. In establishing monitoring regulations, EPA must specify the frequency of monitoring, test methods, and reporting requirements.

Training

Within two years of enactment, EPA must issue a model state program for training operators of incinerators. State programs must be at least as effective as EPA's model. Within three years of the issuance of standards and guidelines for a specific category, any individual who has control over any process that affects emissions from such a unit must have completed a qualified training program.

Permits

Within three years of promulgation of a performance standard for an incinerator category, any unit in that category must possess a permit under Title V. The permit program makes it unlawful to operate an affected source. EPA is required, within 12 months, to identify the minimum elements to be included in a permit program to be administered by an air pollution control agency. Such programs must include, among other things, requirements for permit applications, monitoring and reporting requirements, permit fee authority, requirements for adequate personnel and funding, and authority for issuing and processing permits.

States are required within three years of enactment to submit to EPA a permit program, including a legal opinion that the state has adequate authority to implement the program. The EPA Administrator is required to approve or disapprove the program not later than one year after receiving it. The Act allows for partial permit programs, as well as for interim approval for up to two years.

Sources are required to obtain a permit by the effective date of the permit program. Sources subject to the permit program must submit with their applications a compliance plan, including a schedule of compliance and a schedule for the permittee to submit progress reports. Permitting authorities must approve or disapprove a completed application and issue or deny the permit within 18 months after receiving it. Sources must certify, at least annually, that they are in compliance with the requirements for their permits.

Permits must include enforceable emission limits and standards, a compliance schedule, and requirements for the source to submit semiannual reports on the results of required monitoring. In addition, permits must specify inspection, compliance certification, and reporting requirements (STAPPA/ALAPCO, 1990).

EPA also is required to conduct an audit, at least every two years, of each permitting program and is provided with the authority to terminate, modify, or revoke and reissue permits. Any permitting authority may establish additional, more stringent permitting requirements as long as such requirements are not inconsistent with the Act.

REFERENCES

Code of Federal Regulations, July 1, 1990. 40 Parts 264 and 265, revised.

ENSR, 1990. RCRA Handbook. A Guide to Permitting, Compliance, Closure and Corrective Action under RCRA, prepared by ENSR Consulting and Engineering, third edition, pp. 66, 91, 105.

Federal Register, July 22, 1991. Hazardous Waste TSDFs; Organic Air Emission Standards; EPA Proposed Rule. Vol. 56, No. 140, pp. 33490–33511, 33536, and 33539.

STAPPA/ALAPCO, 1990. Summary of the Clean Air Act Amendments of 1990 prepared by the State and Territorial Air Pollution Program Administrators and the Association of Local Air Pollution Control Officials, Washington, D.C., pp. 15–21, and 25–26.

The Clean Air Act Amendments, Title III as of Nov. 15, 1990 (CAAA).

The Comprehensive Environmental Response, Compensation, and Liability Act of 1990 (CERCLA).

The Superfund Amendments and Reauthorization Act of 1986 (SARA).

U.S. EPA, 1991. Implementation Strategy for the Clean Air Act Amendments of 1990. Office of Air and Radiation, Washington, D.C., pp. 13–40, and B-8.

5

Measurement and Monitoring Approaches for Assessing VOC Emission Rate

The goal of this chapter is to introduce various measurement and monitoring approaches for assessing the volatile organic compound (VOC) emission rate from waste treatment and disposal facilities. Because there are a variety of approaches for assessing the emission rate and the selection of the most suitable approach is heavily influenced by the emission source, our discussion of VOC emission assessment approaches must begin with these emission sources. This discussion is limited to published emission assessment technologies.

As described in Chapter 3, VOC emission sources can be described as one of three types of sources: uncontrolled sources (uncovered landfills, open lagoons, contaminated soils, open tanks, containerized uncovered materials); remediation sources (soils handling, air strippers, incinerators, in situ venting, solidification/stabilization processes, other treatment processes); and controlled sources (covered landfills, covered lagoons, covered tanks, containerized covered materials, leaks from process controls). But to an environmental scientist responsible for assessing the emission rate, there are only two classes of sources: point sources (all covered, vented processes); and area sources (all uncovered, nonvented fugitive sources). This classification is based on the emission assessment approach rather than the process, emission control measure, or regulation. Table 5-1 lists various VOC emission sources as point and area sources, and possible candidate assessment technologies also are provided. It is this emission source classification (point or area source) that will determine the emission assessment strategy used. The various measurement and modeling approaches are presented below, with discussions about why a particular approach or technology has application for a given source. A summary of applications of emission rate assessment approaches is given in Table 5-2.

INTRODUCTION

Assessment of the emission rate of VOCs from waste treatment and disposal facilities presents a variety of challenges to environmental scientists. Emission rate data are preferred over concentration data (mass/volume) for most applications because emission rate data can be used for many purposes including health risk assessment and the design of emission control technologies. However, the most common usage of emission rate data is to determine yearly emissions of VOCs (mass/year) per emission source. Emission rate data thus are useful for assessing long-term air quality impacts.

There are many acceptable approaches for assessing emissions from area sources. Recently, EPA has published technical guidance manuals and formalized the approach for conducting air pathway analysis (APA) at hazardous sites. This effort is in support of site restoration activities, including conducting exposure assessments for undisturbed and disturbed (i.e., during remediation) waste sites (U.S. EPA, Vols. 1–4, 1989). Although written for the assessment of emissions from uncontrolled hazardous waste sources (Superfund hazardous waste landfills and lagoons), the technologies described are applicable to any area or fugitive source. Volume 2 of this four-volume guidance series focuses on estimating the emission rate from area sources such as hazardous waste landfills and lagoons (EPA, Vol. 2, 1989). The emission assessment approaches and the respective technologies described in Volume 2 include direct emission measurement, indirect emission measurement, fenceline (air) monitoring and modeling, and predictive modeling. The first three of these measurement approaches for measuring or estimating the emission rate, as described in APA Volume 2 and their respective assessment technologies, are discussed below (paraphrased from Vol. 2).

Several factors determine which technology or combination of technologies is appropriate for evaluating a given site; and some sources actually are a combination of sources (e.g., point and area sources or multiple area/fugitive sources), necessitating the use of several assessment technologies to generate representative emission rate data. The determining factors include an a priori estimate of the compounds emitted and the emission rates, the level of effort available to determine these emission rates, the degree of accuracy required, and the complexity of the source.

An important distinction needed for an understanding of the emission rate (mass/time) measurement technologies is that of whether the technol-

TABLE 5-1. Summary of area and point sources and candidate assessment technologies.

	Direct Measure							Indirect Measure							Air Monitor/Model		
	Vent	Flux chamber	Head space	Wind tunnel	Subsurface flux	Optical remote	C.P.	Transect	Up/down wind	Mass balance	x-wind	Boundary	Optical remote	Tracers	Integrated sample	Cont. monitoring point	Cont. monitoring line
Area Sources																	
Open tanks																	
Quiescent	O[a]	O						O	O		O			O			
Agitated/aerated	O[a]	O		O		O	O	O	O	O	O		O	O			
Surface impoundments/lagoons																	
Quiescent		O						O	O		O	O		O	O	O	O
Agitated/aerated		O		O		O	O	O	O	O	O	O	O	O	O	O	O
Fugitive process leaks		O	O					O	O					O	O	O	O
Landfills																	
Uncovered		O	O		O			O	O		O	O					
Temporary/failed cover		O	O	O	O			O	O		O	O					

Open containers[a]
Storage piles[a]
Open treatment process[a]
Land treatment
Spill areas
Point Sources
Open tanks
Closed vented landfill
(Landfill/subsurface waste)
Covered vented treatment process
Solidify/stabilize
Chemical treatment
Covered unvented tanks
Classic point sources
Air strippers
Incinerators
Process vents
Distillation
Fractionation
Evaporation
Solvent extraction
Steam stripping

[a] Cover and duct if possible
C.P.—Concentration Profile Technology
Cont.—Continuous

TABLE 5-2. Application of emission rate measurement approaches to area emission sources.

Area Source Emission Assessment	Area Source	Limitations/Comments
Vent	All process vents	Must have measurable gas flow
Surface isolation flux chamber	Active landfills Inactive landfills Surface impoundments Land treatment	Limited to small cells with uniform waste composition Can be used on surface and for vents at inactive landfills Must float equipment Subject to treatment cycle variabilities
Head space sample	Applications similar to the surface isolation flux chamber	Typical use for concentration measurements; data used for relative comparison purposes
Wind tunnels	Inactive controlled and uncontrolled landfills Surface impoundments Waste piles	Used to estimate emissions under simulated wind flow Can be difficult to perform sampling because of air supply needs Provides estimates of particulate matter emissions
Subsurface direct emission measurement technologies	Inactive controlled and uncontrolled landfills Subsurface contamination	Used to measure soil gas concentration or emission rates subsurface Typically used to identify and map subsurface contaminants via soil gas concentration; can be used to estimate emissions from disturbed waste conditions
Concentration profile technique	Surface impoundments, land treatment	Requires complex equipment; meteorological conditions must meet criteria; not suited for small impoundments or land treatment plots
Transect technique	Active landfills, surface impoundments, land treatment, drum storage	Meteorological conditions must meet criteria; requires minimal interferences from other upwind sources
Upwind/downwind technique	All treatment facilities and uncontrolled waste sites	Emission estimate limited; technique typically used as survey technique in the development of a program to more accurately represent emissions
Cross wind	Most facilities/sites	Geometry of source significant
Boundary layer	Most facilities/sites	Challenging application
Mass balance technique	Most treatment facilities, process units	Must identify and be capable of measuring all streams
Tracers	Any liquid process	Sample- and labor-intensive
Air monitoring/modeling technologies	Treatment facilities or hazardous waste site fenceline	Meteorological conditions, terrain, and upwind interferences will affect utility; analytical sensitivity usually a limiting factor

Reference: U.S. EPA, 1989, Volume 2.

ogy directly measures the emission flux (rate/area or mass/time, area) of a VOC at the source or measures the effect of the emission event (ambient concentration of the VOC). Technologies that directly measure the emission event must measure all the parameters necessary to calculate an emission rate. An emission rate (mass/time) can be calculated by multiplying the emission flux rate (mass/time, area) by the surface area responsible for the emission event. Most technologies that measure the ambient concentration must use an interpretation (such as dispersion modeling) to determine the associated emission rate. Other methods calculate the pollutant concentration in such a way that the emission is not directly related to a given area or time interval. These technologies typically use air dispersion modeling to indicate the emission rate responsible for the emission concentration that is measured, given the unique source, dispersion, and transport conditions of the testing.

Definitions of emission assessment approaches or technologies, sample collection techniques, and analytical methodologies are necessary for the following discussion. The emission assessment approach or technology is the technical approach or scheme used to estimate emissions that incorporate sample collection and the analysis of samples. There are three emission measurement approaches: direct measurement, indirect measurement, and air monitoring (or fenceline monitoring) and modeling. These approaches, which are composed of several technologies within these categories, are very different. Each type of technology has unique advantages and disadvantages, so that there is one best approach or technology per application. The sample collection technique is the means by which the gas or atmospheric sample is collected and supplied to the laboratory for analysis. There also are options for the analysis, depending on the analytes of interest, the expected concentration range, the desired level of accuracy, and the data quality objectives of the assessment. Most emission assessment approaches will involve all three components: an emission assessment technology, a sample collection technique, and an analytical methodology. The exceptions are some instrumental techniques, which usually employ continuous instruments or monitors and draw in sample at the inlet or monitor the ambient VOC concentration with optical techniques. Some instrumental techniques use sample conditioning, but none uses an independent collection medium per se (canister, solid sorbent, bag, syringe, impinger).

This concept of emission assessment technology, sample collection, and analytical methodology is illustrated in Figure 5-1. Three common assessment technologies are shown, representing each of the three classes of assessment technology. All are capable of assessing the emission rate from the VOC source (open tank). All three technologies are shown using

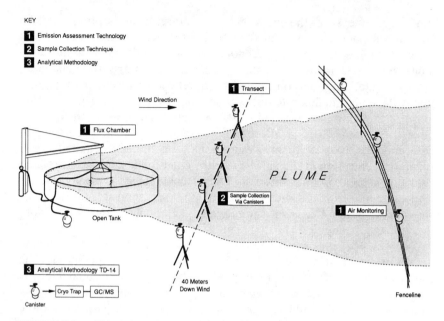

FIGURE 5-1.   Illustration of emission assessment technology, sample collection technique, and analytical methodology.

the same sample collection technique, namely, evacuated stainless steel canisters operated in the vacuum mode. Also the analytical methodology is the same for all three approaches, namely, EPA Method TO-14 gas chromatography with mass spectroscopy (GC/MS). There are a variety of sample collection techniques and analytical methodologies available for use, but EPA TO-14 is widely used and is a preferred methodology for VOCs. An instrumental technique could replace the sample collection technique and analytical methodology (e.g., a continuous gas monitor at the fenceline or optical remote sensing for all three emission assessment technologies), but one of the three emission assessment technologies is needed regardless of the sample collection technique and the analytical methodology used.

ASSESSMENT APPROACHES

Direct Emission Measurement

The direct emission measurement approach often is the preferred approach for assessing VOC emissions from waste treatment processes and other area sources. This is so for several reasons: the technologies are relatively easy to use; they are source-specific, allowing for the assessment of single processes at sites with multiple VOC emission sources (i.e., no upwind interferences); they are not significantly influenced by meteorological conditions; and they do not require modeling in order to estimate emissions.

Direct emission measurement of covered and vented processes is straightforward, and the assessment is made by measuring the gas velocity, the vent cross-sectional area, and the concentration of VOCs in the vent gas. This approach is the standard vent or stack sampling technology and provides an accurate and reliable emission assessment.

Direct emissions measurement for area (landfill or lagoon) or fugitive (process vent leaks) sources consists of measuring the gas concentration, flow rate, and surface emissions area for the emission event at the emitting surface prior to dispersion into the atmosphere. Air typically is purged into the enclosed chamber as a carrier gas or sweep air. Technologies applicable to volatile emission rate measurements from surfaces are the surface emissions isolation flux chamber (Balfour, Schmidt, Eklund, Eklund et al. 1985, 1987; DuPont, 1987; Radian, 1986; Schmidt and Balfour, 1983), head space samplers (Kapling et al., 1986), and wind tunnels (Cowherd, 1985). Cracks in surface covers also may be sampled by these technologies (Schmidt and Clark, 1990). Vents at uncontrolled hazardous waste sites typically have minimal or no flow and may be sampled by the above technologies or by head space emissions concentration measurements (Wood and Porter, 1986). Where measurable gas flow velocities are present, vent emission rates can be sampled by standard stack sampling methods.

The volatile emission flux for subsurface soils can be measured using the downhole isolation flux chamber (Schmidt and Balfour, 1983), soil probes (Kerfoot, 1987), and vapor monitoring wells (Schmidt et al., 1986). These technologies are similar to the surface emissions isolation flux chamber technology described in the following subsection and can generate volatile emission rate data representative of "disturbed" waste conditions. When used without "sweep air," these technologies help measure the soil gas or ambient concentration rather than the emission rate.

Vent Sampling

Assessment of emissions from covered and vented processes using the standard vent or stack sampling technology is straightforward. As with all direct measurement technologies, all parameters are measured, including the vent diameter (or vent cross-sectional area), the gas velocity, and the vent gas concentration. With the exception of the thermal destruction treatment process (pyrolysis, incineration), most of the process vents encountered in these waste treatment and disposal facilities are at a low temperature and a low pressure; so sample conditioning usually is not required, and the sampling train generally consists of a clean, rigid tube as the probe in the vent, inert (nonlined) flexible tubing, and the sample collection medium or instrument. The vent should be approached by following EPA protocols for velocity traverses, flow rate, and moisture (EPA Methods 1, 2, and 4). However, the measurement effort will focus on the VOC sample collection technique and analytical methodology (see below, this chapter). With liquid treatment processes, moisture may interfere with the sample collection or analysis; so each source should be evaluated to determine whether or not a moisture knockout trap is necessary.

Because point source emission assessment is very clear-cut and the resulting emission assessment generally is highly accurate, precise, and representative, an approach that should be considered for uncovered, unducted sources (especially pilot-scale waste treatment processes) is covering, ducting, and ventilating the source for the emission assessment. This approach of modifying the source for the emission assessment may yield low-cost, high-quality emission estimate data using only limited assessment capabilities.

Surface Emission Isolation Flux Chamber

The surface emissions isolation flux chamber is one of the most promising technologies for the direct measurement of VOC emissions. Guidelines have been developed by EPA for application of this methodology to land surfaces (Radian, 1986), and it also is applicable to liquid surfaces (Eklund et al., 1985, 1987). The technology uses a chamber to isolate a known surface area for emissions measurement. Clean, dry sweep air is added to the chamber at a metered rate; and within the chamber, the sweep air is mixed with emitted vapors and gases by the physical design of the sweep air inlet and/or an impeller. The concentration of the exhaust gas is measured at the chamber outlet for specific VOCs by real-time instruments and/or usually is collected as a sample for laboratory analysis. A diagram of a flux chamber apparatus is shown in Figure 5-2. The emission flux can be calculated as:

$$E_i = \frac{C_i Q}{A} \qquad (5\text{-}1)$$

where E_i = emission rate of component i ($\mu g/m^2$-min); C_i = concentration of component i ($\mu g/m^3$); Q = sweep air flow rate into chamber (m^3/min); and A = surface area enclosed by the chamber (m^2).

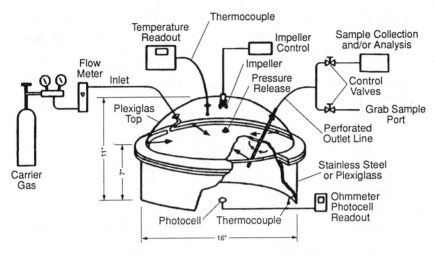

FIGURE 5-2. Cutaway side view of emission isolation flux chamber sampling apparatus. (*Source:* Radian, 1986)

Statistical methods are used to determine the number of measurements required to characterize the emissions from an area source. These methods are based on the source surface area and the variability of the measured emission rate at randomly selected locations across the site. The principal advantages of this technology are that an emission rate can be measured in the field without modeling, and the field personnel can control the testing conditions. The area source measurement is made at the emitting surface, whether the surface is a solid, a liquid, an opening (crack), or a vent. The principal disadvantage is that the measurement is made over a relatively small area, and numerous measurements may be necessary to characterize an emission source. Also, the emission flux may be enhanced or suppressed in the process of performing the measurement, thus altering the emission event.

The EPA-recommended flux chamber technology as described in the literature can be applied to a variety of area sources with only minor adaptions and equipment modifications. The following subsections describe the applications of the technology to land surfaces, to nonaerated, nonmixed liquid surfaces, to aerated and mixed liquid surfaces, and to fugitive process emission sources.

Land Surfaces
The flux chamber was designed and tested for land surfaces where the volatile/semivolatile source (waste material) is on the surface or is in a

subsurface. The difference between surface and subsurface applications is that for direct contact with the waste, emission rates generally are greater and those rates often are subject to influences such as solar heating, ambient temperature, surface moisture, and physical disturbance of the waste material. Where the waste material is subsurface (below land surface) and the volatile species must migrate through a layer of soil, the emission rates can be lower and often are not affected by surface conditions or activity.

Assessing VOC species emissions from surface waste sources such as landfills, stockpiled waste, and land farms is a straightforward and common application of the technology. Because the chamber will be in contact with the waste, contamination of equipment and cross-contamination are concerns. These problems can be addressed by cleaning the chamber walls where contact with waste has been made and back-flushing the chamber exhaust or sample line. One approach is to avoid contact by wrapping the chamber lip with wide, disposable Teflon tape use and preventing contact with solid waste material. Care must be taken to not introduce into the chamber materials such as adhesive tape that might off-gas contaminate species. All wrapping must be secured outside the chamber. In addition to cleaning and limiting contact with the waste, more frequent (10–20%) blank testing is recommended for testing with waste contact.

Nonaerated, Nonmixed Liquid Surfaces

Application of the technology to liquid surfaces requires floating or suspending the chamber on/over the liquid surface Eklund (Eklund et al., 1987) and (Schmidt, Faught and Nottoli, 1991). For nonaerated and non-mixed liquid surfaces such as abandoned lagoons and ponds, quality assurance testing has demonstrated that lower emission rates will result if the chamber lip significantly penetrates the liquid surface and prevents communication of the isolated surface with the waste body (Gholson et al., 1988). In nonmixed liquid systems, natural mixing occurs by heating and cooling of the surface layer and the resulting convective mixing. If the chamber contains a layer of trapped liquid, the volatile species may diffuse, and the resulting liquid layer may retard emissions. This could produce a bias in the test data (in this case, a negative bias), which can be prevented by suspending the chamber and keeping the chamber lip floating just under the liquid surface. Flotation/suspension systems (Figure 5-3) have been designed and used successfully (Eklund et al., 1987). Aside from this concern, liquid testing can be accomplished by following the testing protocol as described for land surfaces, including spatial and temporal test strategies.

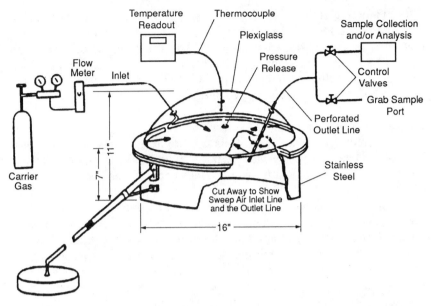

FIGURE 5-3.   Cutaway diagram of the surface emission isolation flux chamber and support equipment for liquid surfaces.   (*Source:* Eklund, et al., 1987)

Aerated, Mixed Liquid Surfaces

Aerated and/or mixed surfaces, usually associated with a treatment process such as municipal sewage or industrial waste water treatment, are tested by using the flux chamber as it is used for quiescent surfaces (Schmidt and Faught, 1990; Schmidt et al., 1991). Mixed liquid surfaces usually prevent a low bias in the emission estimate by continually renewing the liquid surface. For vigorous mixing, it may be necessary to attach flotation devices to the chamber to improve the stability of the equipment, thus preventing chamber upset.

Aerated surfaces are unique in that bulk air flow from the system strips volatile species and carries contaminants into the chamber. This air flow must be measured and used in the calculation for determining the emission rate. The aeration flow can be measured by attaching a volume-calibrated, deflated plastic bag to the chamber pressure port, sealing all other ports, and timing the bag filling (Schmidt and Faught, 1990). Dividing the bag volume by the filling rate gives the aeration flow rate. The aeration rate also can be measured by using a pump and a manometer to match the flow rate at a zero pressure difference, and by using a mass flow measuring device such as a rotameter.

In evaluating emissions from an aerated treatment process, both aerated and nonaerated zones must be assessed independently. The average unit emission rate from each zone and the estimated surface area are needed to assess emissions from each zone. Soil biofilters with forced aeration, which are aerated systems similar to aeration basins, also have been tested using this technology (Berry et al., 1991).

Process Fugitive Seam/Leak Assessment

The flux chamber technology can be used to assess emissions from passive vents, seams, leaking valves, ports, and cracks in control devices ranging from fixed and floating roofs to clay caps on landfills (Schmidt and Clark, 1990). These applications require modifications to the standard protocol: (1) the chamber must be adapted to the fugitive source, and (2) the process or source must be well understood for investigators to properly design a testing strategy and assess the area source. Adapting the chamber to these fugitive emission sources can be as simple as placing the chamber on a flat seam or as involved as constructing an adaptor to interface with the port, valve, or process opening. When possible, these adapters should be made from inert materials, and the entire system should be blank-tested. Operating conditions such as flow rate and residence time parameters may need to be changed because of the increased enclosure volume.

The requirement of representative testing, however, is a particular challenge for this application. Typically, process seam/fugitive emissions first are surveyed with real-time analyzers, and all fugitive emissions are identified, organized into zones or ranges of similar emission potential, and tested as zones of emissions potential, as described for land surfaces. An estimate of emissions can be obtained by averaging the emission rate per zone and calculating emissions per zone by knowing the number of sources, area of the sources, or linear feet of the sources. Unit emission rate data for this type of source can have units such as mass per time per vent or foot of seam leak (Schmidt and Clark, 1990).

Head Space Samplers

Head space samplers are surface isolation chambers that measure the quantity or concentration of emitted vapors and/or gas that builds up in the chamber over a period of time rather than the emission flux for a given time. Thus there is no flow rate measurement, and the exposure time component is used to estimate the rate. This technology usually is considered to be limited to a screening technology because of inaccuracies inherent in it. The true emissions may be suppressed by the back-pressure of the VOCs in the head space, resulting in an undetermined negative bias of the assessment.

Head space samplers may be operated in one of two modes, herein referred to as static and dynamic modes. In the static mode, the sampling enclosure is placed over the emitting surface for a given period of time (Batterman et al., 1991; Kapling et al., 1986). This is the most common use of the technique, generating concentration data that are used for relative evaluation purposes. The enclosure may be purged initially with clean air or nitrogen. Then emissions are allowed to concentrate in the chamber for later withdrawal to sampling media. This mode makes detection easier because the emissions concentration increases over time. Its principal disadvantage is that the emission flux may decrease as the concentration within the enclosure increases because the concentration gradient from the soil gas to the air interface is reduced (the calculated emission rate is biased low). The head space sampler approach has not been validated. The emission flux is calculated as:

$$E_i = \frac{C_i V_E}{tA} \tag{5-2}$$

where E_i = emission rate of component i (μg/m²-s), C_i = concentration of component i (μg/m³), V_E = volume of the enclosure (m³), t = length of time enclosure is in place (s), and A = surface area enclosed by chamber (m²).

In the dynamic mode, the sampling enclosure is placed over the emitting surface, and sample is withdrawn continuously from the enclosure (Kapling et al., 1986). The emitted species is concentrated on sampling media to increase the ability of the analytical method to detect air contaminants, or the operation may be continuously monitored as is done for the emission isolation flux chamber. The disadvantage of operating in the dynamic mode is that, as the atmosphere within the enclosure is withdrawn, the emission rate value may be affected by the addition of bulk flow of the soil gas into the chamber or, alternately, by air trapping occurring within the enclosure because of leakage at the enclosure's bottom edge, or by air sweeping through the soil at the enclosure's bottom edge. When the sample is concentrated on the sampling media (i.e., sorbent), the emission flux is calculated as:

$$E_i = \frac{C_i V_s}{At} \tag{5-3}$$

where E_i = emission rate of component i (μg/m²-sec), C_i = concentration of component i (μg/m³), V_s = total volume of sample withdrawn (m³), t = length of sampling interval (s), and A = surface area enclosed by chamber (m²).

Wind Tunnels

The Astle wind tunnel is a form of surface enclosure developed for "measurement of odor source strength" (Astle et al., 1982), but it is applicable to VOC emissions measurement. This portable wind tunnel (Figure 5-4) consists of an open-bottom enclosure that is placed on the emitting surface. Ambient air is blown through the chamber at typical wind speed rates (e.g., 1 to 15 mph or 0.5 to 6.7 m/sec) and collected near the outlet. The enclosure differs from the surface emission isolation flux chamber described above in that it simulates wind flow, allowing the measurement of emissions under varying wind conditions. However, test results for VOC emissions rate measurement were not identified in the literature. The emission flux calculation is:

$$E_i = \frac{C_i Q}{A} \tag{5-1}$$

where E_i = emission rate of component i (μg/m^2-sec); C_i = concentration of component i (μg/m^3); Q = air flow rate through tunnel (m^3/sec); and A = surface area enclosed by the chamber (m^2).

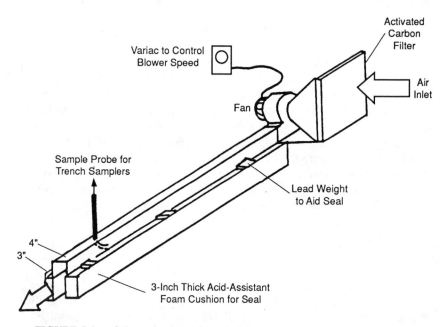

FIGURE 5-4.   Schematic of portable wind tunnel.   (*Source:* U.S. EPA, 1989)

Subsurface Direct Emission
Measurement Technologies

Direct emission measurement technologies that have applications for measuring emissions from subsurface waste include the downhole isolation flux chamber (Figure 5-5), soil probes (Figure 5-6), and vapor monitoring wells (Figure 5-7). Each is used to measure the emission rate or the

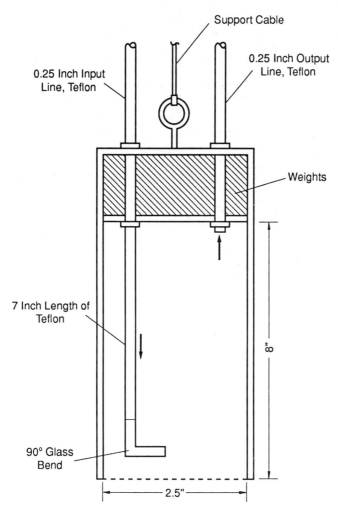

FIGURE 5-5.   Schematic diagram of the downhole emissions flux chamber.   (*Source:* Schmidt and Balfour, 1983)

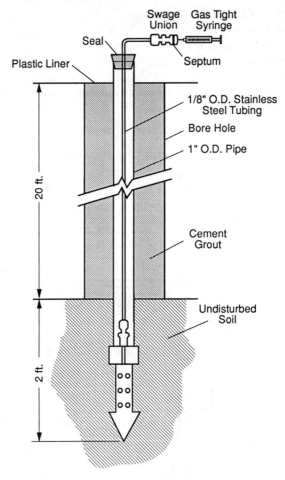

FIGURE 5-6.   Schematic diagram of vapor sampling probe.   (*Source:* U.S. EPA, 1989)

gas concentration at some depth below the land surface by placing an enclosed chamber within the soil or on an exposed surface at depth (i.e., during drilling operations). All three technologies can be operated by utilizing sweep air in a manner similar to that of the surface isolation flux chamber and can provide a direct measurement of the subsurface soils emission rate potential. These technologies also can be used without sweep air, like head space samplers, to measure the soil pore gas concentration. The advantage of using these technologies is that the emission's concentration within the soil pores is higher than in the atmosphere above

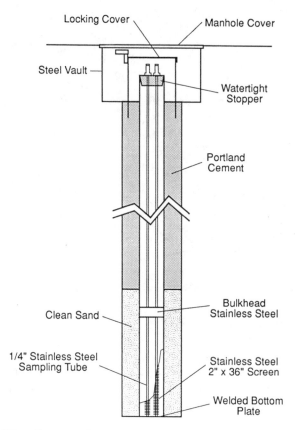

FIGURE 5-7.   Vapor monitoring well construction.   (*Source:* U.S. EPA, 1989)

the site; therefore, they can provide lower detection limits than other technologies. The soil pore space concentration data can be used as an input to the predictive modeling.

Direct Emission Assessment
Using Optical Remote Sensing

A new approach to direct emission assessment involves the use of optical remote sensing, typically FTIR or UV open path remote sensing (Bath et al., 1989). This technique requires an array of vertically spaced light beams oriented to transect the downwind contaminant plume (Figure 5-8) so that the array contains the plume (Whitcraft and Wood, 1990). The wind speed and direction are measured along each transect, and the optical remote sensor simultaneously monitors for selected species (path-integrated concentration) at each transect height. The resulting wind vec-

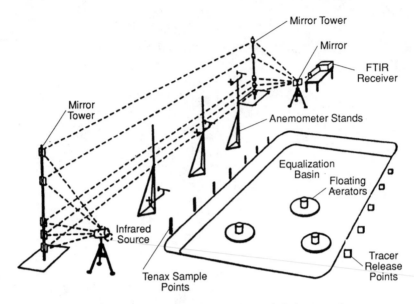

FIGURE 5-8.   FTIR equipment arrangement for downwind plume monitoring.   (*Source:* Whitcraft and Wood, 1990)

tor at right angles to the transect and the path-integrated concentrations then are used to calculate the emission rate. This approach is analogous to stack testing where the concentration and the stack gas velocity are used to assess the emission rate.

This application of optical remote sensing offers advantages over some other approaches (e.g., indirect measurement, fenceline monitoring/modeling) and some direct measurement technologies. It will allow for assessment of the source in question without accessing the emitting surface, which makes this direct technology unique. This is an advantage for sources that are difficult to access or are heterogeneous. Because this technology path-integrates the emissions from the entire source, the issue of representative spatially distributed sampling is avoided. In a sense, this technology combines the principal advantages of both direct (no modeling required; limited meteorological influences) and indirect (no spatially-distributed sampling; applicability for complex sources/heterogeneous sources; no access required) assessment technologies. In addition, large amounts of data can be collected on-site with rapid or essentially real-time data generation.

Unfortunately, the technology also has some of the disadvantages of both direct and indirect technologies. The application of this direct assessment technology will be determined by the availability of optical remote sensing instrumentation, the type and the level of the VOCs emitted, and the type and the level of upwind interferences at the source location. This technology also is somewhat dependent on weather conditions, in that the location and the shape of the plume are determined by meteorological factors. This unique direct assessment technology is preferred over others for sources that are heterogeneous and complex and/or may involve activities such as aeration, mixing, or dynamic treatment, provided that the sensing technology used can detect the VOCs of interest at the source strength at which the VOCs are emitted.

Indirect Emission Measurement

Several indirect emission measurement technologies have been identified, including concentration profile technology (Balfour et al., 1984; Thibodeaux et al., 1982), transect technology (Balfour et al., 1984; Farmer et al., 1980), upwind/downwind technology (Hwang, 1982, 1985), mass balance (Balfour et al., 1984), cross-wind sampling (Wisner and Davis, 1989), boundary-layer sampling (Esplin, 1988), and remote sensing McLaren and Stedman, 1990; Scotto et al., 1990; Spellicy et al., 1991; U.S. EPA, Vol. 2, 1989). These technologies (except mass balance) generally consist of measuring the atmospheric concentration of the emitted species and then determining the emission rate by modeling. Many of the models were developed to determine downwind concentrations resulting from stack or point source emissions. The emission area source is considered to be a point source. For area emission sources, the source is modeled as a virtual point source. These technologies produce an overall emission rate estimate for a given area source. The indirect technologies require meteorological monitoring to properly align the sampling systems and to reduce the data following sample analysis.

A disadvantage of indirect emission measurement technologies is that they are dependent on meteorological conditions; changes in those conditions will significantly affect the investigator's ability to collect useful data. Unacceptable meteorological conditions may invalidate much of the data collected, requiring an additional sampling effort. These technologies also may not be applicable at some sites where the source area is excessively large or where insufficient space exists downwind to set up the sampling array. The use of indirect technologies can be enhanced by using tracer gases released at known rates at the source. The dilution ratio of the tracer then can be used to empirically model the VOC emission rate.

Concentration Profile
The concentration profile (C-P) technology requires the measurement of the emitted species concentration at logarithmical spaced heights at a

downwind location on the plume centerline. This technology has been tested under a variety of waste site conditions and has been shown to produce reasonably valid results.

The C-P technology was developed by L. J. Thibodeaux and co-workers at the University of Arkansas under an EPA contract (Thibodeaux et al., 1982). The technology is based on measurements of wind velocity, volatile species concentration, and temperature profiles in the boundary layer above the waste body. These measurements are used to estimate the vertical flux of the volatile species as:

$$E_i = \left[\frac{D_i}{D_{H_2O}}\right]^n \frac{S_v S_i K^2}{\phi_m^2 S_c} \tag{5-4}$$

where E_i = emission rate (flux) of organic species, i (g/cm²-sec); D_i = molecular diffusivity of water vapor in air (cm²/sec); K = von Karman's constant; S_v = logarithmic slope of the air velocity profile (cm/sec); S_i = logarithmic slope of the concentration profile for organic species, i (g/cm³); ϕ_m = Businger wind shear parameter; S_c = turbulent Schmidt number, and n = exponent for diffusivity ratio.

The term $\phi_m^2 S_c$ represents an atmospheric stability correction factor and is expressed as a function of the Richardson number. The function is an empirical correlation that corrects the estimated emission rate for water vapor to measured values under various atmospheric stabilities. For this reason, the correction factor is valid only under specific meteorological conditions. The sampling equipment, shown in Figure 5-9, consists of a 4-m mast with a wind direction indicator, wind speed sensors, temperature sensors, and air collection probes at six logarithmical spaced heights above the area source; a continuous real-time data collection system; and a thermocouple for measuring temperature. Prior to sample collection, meteorological conditions must be monitored to determine compliance with the necessary meteorological criteria. Once acceptable meteorological conditions are documented, the sample collection period is initiated. During the sample collection period, wind speed, air temperature, and relative humidity are measured.

Transect
The transect technology, which measures the concentration of VOCs at several locations perpendicular to the plume centerline, has been satisfactorily tested at a variety of waste treatment facilities and waste sites. This technology is an indirect emission measurement approach that has been used to measure fugitive particulate and gaseous emissions from area and line sources (Farmer et al., 1980). The technique has been applied to

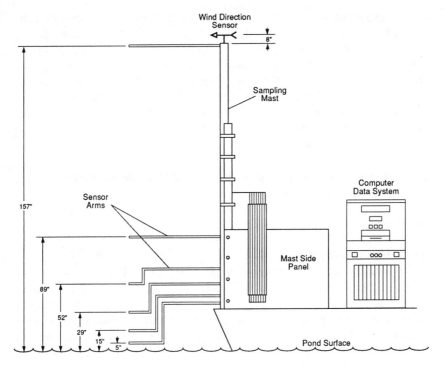

FIGURE 5-9.   Mast sample collection system for C-P sampling.   (*Source:* U.S. EPA, 1989)

landfills, surface impoundments, and waste handling/treatment operations. Horizontal and vertical arrays of samplers are used to measure concentrations of species within the effective cross section of the fugitive emission plume. The VOC emission rate then is obtained by spatial integration of the measured concentrations over the assumed plume area (Balfour et al., 1984):

$$E_i = \frac{u}{A_s} \iint_{Ap} C_{i(h,w)} dh \ dw \qquad (5\text{-}5)$$

where E_i = emission rate of component i (μg/m²-sec); u = wind speed (m/sec); C_i = concentration of component i at point (h,w), corrected for upwind background (μg/m³); h = vertical distance coordinate (m); w = horizontal distance coordinate (m); A_s = surface area of emitting source (m²); and A_p = effective cross-sectional area of plume (m²).

The sampling equipment consists of a central 3.5-m mast having three equally spaced air sampling probes, single wind direction, wind speed, and temperature sensors at the top, and five 1.5-m masts with single air sampling probes. The central mast is aligned with the expected plume centerline. Two masts are placed at equal spacings on each side of the central mast, and one mast is used to collect air samples at an upwind location. The spacing of the associated masts is selected to cover the expected horizontal plume cross section, as defined by observation and/ or profiling with real-time analyzers. Prior to sample collection, meteorological parameters must be monitored to determine if acceptable sampling conditions exist. A diagram of a transect sampling system is shown in Figure 5-10.

The transect is somewhat less susceptible to changing meteorological conditions compared to the C-P approach and is easier to implement, but it does not account for the vertical dispersion of the emitted species due to their varying molecular weights.

Upwind/Downwind

The upwind/downwind technology (Hwang, 1982, 1985) measures the VOCs at single upwind and downwind locations. This technology has a much higher degree of uncertainty than the two previous technologies because of its limited number of sampling points and its lack of a sampling specific model. It does allow for the collection of data at reduced time and cost compared to the other technologies. The upwind/downwind technique frequently is used for screening and not for developing quantitative emission rate data. It is less sophisticated and, therefore, is more straight-

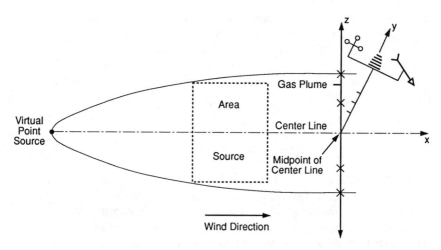

FIGURE 5-10.   Example of transect technique sampling.   (*Source:* U.S. EPA, 1989)

forward to implement; however, it provides very limited measurement data.

Mass Balance

A mass balance technology can be used to indirectly determine emission rates. The technology has been used at disposal facilities where operational data are available, but it is not useful for estimating baseline emission rates at uncontrolled sites. To apply the technology at an uncontrolled site, the concentration of the species in a waste lagoon or contained in the landfill waste would be measured intermittently, and the emission rate would be calculated as the loss of species over time. This technology, although useful for an active system with documented and metered inflows and outflows, generally is limited in application at controlled waste sites. First, most investigators cannot wait for the considerable amount of time required to permit measurable losses of material; second, small losses are difficult to measure because of the sometimes limited precision of the analytical methods available.

Cross-wind Sampling

One approach used to indirectly assess emission rates utilizes a mobile sampling station to traverse the plume in a cross-wind direction (Wisner and Davis, 1989). Integrated air samples are collected from equipment mounted on a flat-bed truck traversing the downwind plume at a constant speed. Meteorological data and site information are used with simple Gaussian plume modeling techniques to predict the emission rate from the fugitive source. The methodology is reported to be insensitive to complex source configurations, variations in wind direction, and the horizontal dispersion rate. The advantage is that it requires fewer sampling stations and samples to characterize a fugitive source as compared to other indirect emission rate testing methodologies. However, there may be some problems associated with this approach, such as the entrainment of road dust and vehicle emission unassociated with the fugitive source in question.

Boundary Layer Emissions Monitoring

A boundary-layer testing method has been proposed for determining the emission rate of contaminants from fugitive sources (Esplin, 1988). It is like the transect technique, but it utilizes a tethered balloon to collect samples continuously at a number of elevations while traversing the boundary layer (vertical direction) of the plume. The approach assumes that the contaminant emission rate and the wind speed/direction are reasonably constant during the sampling period. The objective is to collect samples so that the contaminant concentration profile downwind of the source can be approximated and the flux of contaminants modeled. This approach, although perhaps difficult to implement, should be applicable to testing large, heterogeneous fugitive sources with reasonably accurate estimates of the emission rate.

Remote Sensing

Spectroscopic techniques utilizing collimated light sources (infrared—IR; ultraviolet—UV) are gaining in popularity for characterizing the emission of contaminants from a source, and for characterizing the impact of contaminant release from a source on downwind receptors. Advances in the technology of mobile, long-range spectroscopic techniques have permitted the use of remote sensing as a viable approach to characterize emission from fugitive sources.

Remote sensing, utilizing Fourier-transform infrared (FT-IR), UV, and differential adsorption lidar has been used at sites to characterize the release of contaminants from these sites (Bath et al., 1989; McLaren and Stedman, 1990; Scotto et al., 1990; Spellicy et al., 1991). The approach uses an array of mirrors and these light sources, along with receiving instrumentation, to create a sensing network around a fugitive source. These systems can be used to detect the presence of species, and then to integrate the transport of these species through the network light path to quantitate the emission rate. Meteorological data, along with these data, can be used to model the emission rate using Gaussian plume modeling techniques. As an indirect technology, dispersion modeling is required because the transect array does not fully describe the plume as in the direct assessment technology. Here, the transect is typically a single transect located downwind of the source. The advantage of the approach is that it can provide very comprehensive assessment data because the light path can be established to monitor the downwind plume over the gross extent of the plume and to collect data for long periods of time, affording a large data base for emissions estimation.

Tracer Studies

Tracers can be used as an indirect emission assessment technology, but their use is limited to liquid treatment processes. In most tracer applications, a unique VOC or radioisotope of a representative VOC is added to the liquid treatment process, either in a batch or a continuous mode, and the tracer then is monitored in the downstream liquid stream and as an air emission VOC. These data can be used to develop mass transfer coefficients for labeled VOCs and to estimate VOC emissions from the respective liquid treatment processes. This technology has been used with success at municipal waste water treatment processes, but it can be labor- and resource-intensive, depending on the amount of air and liquid sampling conducted.

Air Monitoring and Modeling

Air monitoring technologies that measure the ambient concentration resulting from area source emissions can be combined with air dispersion modeling to determine the area source emission rate. The primary differences between indirect emission measurement technologies and air monitoring technologies are the distance at which measurements are made from the source, the design of the monitoring network, and the use of these data. Indirect measurements typically are made near the source (usually on-site and within 40 m of the source) and may make it possible to distinguish between multiple source areas on a given site. Air monitoring generally is done at a considerable distance downwind and usually cannot distinguish between multiple emission sources. Typically it measures very low concentrations (e.g., parts per billion-volume) because the contaminant plume is subject to dilution via dispersion with downwind distance.

Periods of time are selected from the air monitoring data base where meteorological conditions and air concentration are known, and these data are used along with an appropriate dispersion model to estimate the source emission rate. A hypothetical emission rate is input into a model simulating the site including the location of air monitors, and the modeled air concentration data are compared to measured air concentration data. The hypothetical emission rate is modified and the process repeated until there is an acceptable match between the modeled and the measured air concentration. This approach, although generally not selected as a first choice for estimating source emissions, can produce useful emission rate estimates. It commonly is used when fenceline VOC and meteorological monitoring is required, and these data are available for use. In this way, a routine air monitoring data set can be used to generate emission rate data.

There are three basic approaches to air monitoring at VOC emission sources: (1) integrated sample collection and off-site analysis using a network of point monitors; (2) continuous, real-time instruments or monitors in a network of point monitors; and (3) continuous, line instruments or monitors (open-path, optical remote sensing) used for "comprehensive" fenceline monitoring. Integrated sample collection and off-site analysis using a network of point monitors is probably the most common technology used, as this technology is straightforward, generally applicable to most sources, and well suited for single or infrequent emission assessment projects. Further, EPA and others have provided protocols for integrated sample collection and analysis of organic compounds, as shown in Table 5-3 (Lodge, 1989; Riggin, 1983; Riggin and Winberry, 1986; Winberry and Murphy, 1989; U.S. EPA, 1983). An air monitoring network is designed, and air concentration samples are collected at fixed and mobile stations as needed to assess the impact at the property fenceline. These data then are used in conjunction with dispersion modeling to estimate the emission rate from the source. One of the more difficult aspects of instituting this technology is selection of the appropriate sample collection technique and analytical methodology. Information on sampling for and analyzing common air contaminants is given in Table 5-4. Again, the advantage of this technology is that simple integrated sampling techniques

TABLE 5-3.   Summary of toxic organic (TO) compendium methods.

Compendium Method	Type of Compound	Sample Collection	Analytical Method
TO-1	Volatile organic compounds	Tenax solid sorbent	GC/MS
TO-2	Volatile organic compounds	Molecular sieve sorbent	GC/MS
TO-3	Volatile organic compounds	Cryotrap	GC/FID
TO-4	Pesticides	Polyurethane foam	GC/ECD
TO-5	Aldehydes/ketones	Impinger	HPLC
TO-6	Phosgene	Impinger	HPLC
TO-7	Amines	Adsorbent	GC/MS
TO-8	Phenols	Impinger	HPLC
TO-9	Dioxins	Polyurathane foam	GC/MS
TO-10	Pesticides	Polyurethane foam	GC/ECD
TO-11	Aldehydes/ketones	Sepelco-PAK	HPLC
TO-12	Nonmethane organic compounds	Canister	FID
TO-13	Polyaromatic hydrocarbons	Polyurethane foam	GC/ECD
TO-14	Volatile organic compounds	Canister	GC/MS

Abbreviations: GC/MS—gas chromatography/mass spectrometry; GC/FID—gas chromatography/flame ionization detector; GC/ECD—gas chromatography/electrolytic conductivity detector; HPLC—high pressure liquid chromatography.
Reference: U.S. EPA, 1990.

TABLE 5-4. Compounds frequently found at hazardous waste sites and useful sampling and analytical information.

Rank (1)	Substance	(2)	SepP IC	Can MS	Adsb MS	Fltr ICP	Puf MS	Otr	Analytical Method (4)	SepP µg/m³	Can ppbv	Adsb ng	Fltr µg/m³	Puf µg/m³
1	TCE	V		+	+				T-GC/MS, C-GC/MS		0.47	0.08	0.0187	
2	Lead	M				+			F-ICAP, F-XR					
3	Toluene	V		+	+				CT-GC/FID, C-GC/MS		0.40	2.0		
4	Benzene	V		+	+				T-GC/MS, C-GC/MS		0.53	2.60		
5	PCBs	SV					+		PUF/XAD2-GC/MS		(b)	(a)		10-6
6	CHCl$_3$	V		+	+				T-GC/MS, C-GC/MS		0.37	0.23		
7	CCl$_2$CCl$_2$	V		+	+				T-GC/MS, C-GC/MS		0.57	2.60		
8	Phenol	SV		+				+	Imp-HPLC, C-GC/MS		(c)	(c)		
9	Arsenic	M						+	F-AA, F-GFAA, F-XR				0.0008	
10	Cadmium	M				+			F-ICAP, F-XR, F-AA				0.0007	
11	Chromium	M				+			F-ICAP, F-AA				0.0017	
12	1,1,1-TCA	V		+	+				T-GC/MS, C-GC/MS		0.42	1.7	0.002	
13	Zinc cpds	M			+	+			F-ICAP, F-AA, F-XR					
14	EtlBenz	V		+	+				T-GC/MS, C-GC/MS		0.44	1.6		
15	Xylenes	V		+	+				T-GC/MS, C-GC/MS		0.31	0.5		
16	CH$_2$Cl$_2$	V		+	+				T-GC/MS, C-GC/MS		0.73	(a)		
17	CHClCHCl	V		+	+			+	T-GC/MS, C-GC/MS		0.10	(a)	0.0079	
18	Mercury	M				+			F-ICAP, CV-AA, ACM				0.0004	
19	Coppers	M				+			F-ICAP, F-AA, F-XR					
20	Cyanides	M						+	F-ISP					
21	CH$_2$CHCl	V		+	+				C-GC/MS		0.42	(a)		
22	(CH$_2$Cl)$_2$	V		+	+				T-GC/MS, C-GC/MS		0.39	3.8		
23	Clrobenz	V		+	+				T-GC/MS, C-GC/MS		0.48	1.7		
24	CHCl$_2$CH$_3$	V		+	+				T-GC/MS, C-GC/MS		0.39	3.8		
25	CCl$_4$	V		+	+				T-GC/MS, C-GC/MS		0.41	0.17		
	Beryllium	M				+			F-ICAP, F-XR		(b)		0.0003	
	Selenium	M				+			F-ICAP, F-XR				0.001	
	Nickel	M				+			F-ICAP, F-XR			(a)	0.002	
	Heptachl	P					+		PUF-GC/ECD, PUF-GC/MS					0.0100
	Acrylonit	V			+			+	T/C-GC/MS					

TABLE 5-4. Compounds frequently found at hazardous waste sites and useful sampling and analytical information (Continued).

Rank (1)	Substance (2)	SepP IC	Can MS	Adsb MS	Fltr ICP	Puf MS	Otr	Analytical Method (4)	SepP µg/m³	Can ppbv	Adsb ng	Fltr µg/m³	Puf µg/m³
	Benzo(a)p	SV					+		PUF/XAD2-HPLC, PUR-XAD2-GC/MS				0.000016	
	Formalde.	V	+						SEP-IC, ACM	0.012				
	1,1,2-TCA	V		+	+				T/C-GC/MS		0.38	2.1		
	Chlordane	P			+		+		PUF-GC/ECD, PUF-C/MS		(b)	(a)		0.0100
	1,1,2,2-T	V		+	+				T/C-GC/MS		(b)	(a)		
	Asbestos	P							F-MICR					
	Mg	M					+		F-ICAP, F-XR			0.0004		
	TriClBen	V		+	+				T/C-GC/MS		(b)	(c)		
	Styrene	V		+	+				T/C-GC/MS		0.45	0.13		
	1,1-DCA	V		+	+				T/C-GC/MS		0.51	5.7		
	EtOxide	V						+	CT-GC/ECD, CT-GD/FID		(b)	(a)		
	DiClBze	V		+	+				T/C-GC/MS		0.32	12.4		
	1,3BuDie	V		+	+				T/C-GC/MS		0.66	(a)		
	Acetone	V	+	+	+				T/C-GC/MS, SEP-IC	0.024	3.3	(c)		
	NitroBz	SV						+	T-GC/MS, PUF/XAD2-GC/MS		(c)	(c)		
	Dei/Aldrn	N,NT						+	PUF-GC/ECD, MS		(c)	(a)		
	HxClCyPDi	SV					+		PUF-GC/ECD, MS		(b)	(a)		0.010
	Acrolein	V	+		+		+		T/C-GC/MS, SEP-IC	0.0229	(b)	(a)		0.00024
	BenzlCl	V		+	+				T/C-GC/MS		(c)	(c)		
	Phosgene	V						+	Imp-HPLC, ACM					
	Nickel	M				+			F-ICAP, F-AA, F-XR					
	EpiClHydn	V			+				T-GC/MS			(a)		
	Acetalyde	V	+		+				Imp-HPLC/UV, SEP-IC		(c)	(c)		
	Parathion	P					+	+	PUF-GC/MS, ECD, NPD		0.02	(a)		
	H₂S	V		+					IMP-COL., GB/FPD, ACM		(b)	(a)	0.0006	
	CH₃Cl	V		+					C-GC/MS, CT-GC/MS		(c)	(a)		
	Coal tar	SV					+	+	PUF-HPLC/UV		0.39	(a)		
	TetrHyFur	V					+	+	T-GC/MS, PUF-GC/MS, C-GC/MS			1.2		10–6

Source: Table taken from the ''Statement of Work for the Analysis of Air Toxics from Superfund Sites.''

Footnotes/abbreviations:

(1) Compounds most frequently found at hazardous waste sites; top 25 listed in order of occurrence.

(2) Classification

    V—volatile

    SV—semivolatile

    M—particulate matter with metal constituents

(3) Notation

    SepP—silica gel doped with 2,4-dinitrophenylhydrazine

    Can—Summa passivated canisters

    Adsb—adsorbent material

    Fltr—filter material such as glass, Teflon, or nylon

    Puf—polyurethane foam plug

    Otr—other sample collection media

    IC—ion chromatography

    MS—mass spectroscopy

    ICP—inductively coupled plasma spectroscopy

(4) Sampling/analytical notation

    ACM—ambient continuous monitor

    C-GC/MS—canister and gas chromatography/mass spectroscopy

    CT-GC/MS—charcoal tube and GC/MS

    CT-GC/FID—charcoal tube and gas chromatography and flame ionization detector

    CV-AA—filter and cold vapor/atomic absorption spectroscopy

    F-AA—filter and AA

    F-GFAA—filter and graphite furnace AA

    F-ICAP—filter and ICP

    F-MICR—filter and microscopy

    F-ISP—filter and ion selective probe

    F-XR—filter and X-ray fluorescence

    Imp-HPLC—impinger and high pressure liquid chromatography

    PUF-XAD2-GC/MS—polyurethane plug/resin, GC/MS

    PUF-GC/ECD—polyurethane plug—gas chromatography and electron capture detector

    SEP-IC—Sepelco-Pak and ion chromatography

    T-GC/MS—Tenax and GC/MS

    T/C-GC/MS—Tenax/Charcoal and GC/MS

    T/C-GC/ECD—Tenax/Charcoal and GC/ECD

    T/C-GC/FID—Tenax/Charcoal and GC/FID

    Imp-HPLC/UV—impinger and high pressure liquid chromatography with ultraviolet detection

(a)—not amenable to Tenax.

(b)—not amenable to canister.

(c)—no detection limits published, but feasible.

    Reference: Winberry and Murphy, 1989.

are used to provide useful data supporting infrequent air monitoring, including emission assessments.

The use of a continuous, real-time monitoring network is an assessment technology much like the use of integrated point monitors, except that the data collection effort is much greater in this case, and the need for air monitoring requires rigorous data collection. The difficulty in designing and operating a continuous monitoring network using real-time instruments is much greater than the effort required for integrated point monitors, but one benefit is realized in the use of these data for estimating emission rates from the source as well as continuous, real-time monitoring ambient air data. Like all technologies in this assessment class, this approach is almost never selected solely to develop emission rates. Typically, continuous monitoring and/or real-time data are required for other reasons; but if this type of air monitoring is to be used for other reasons, these data, along with on-site meteorological data and dispersion modeling, can be used to estimate the emission rate. Meteorological effects, upwind interferences, low ambient concentrations of VOCs as a function of dilution on transport, and the inherent limitations of using dispersion modeling combine to reduce the applicability of air monitoring/modeling for estimating emission rates.

Continuous, real-time monitoring using optical remote sensing is a similar technology, but here the monitoring methodology is very different, warranting a separate discussion. Optical remote sensing or spectroscopic remote sensing encompasses a variety of remote sensing techniques, the most popular of which are listed and described in Table 5-5 (Spellicy et al., 1991). Of these, the most useful techniques for this application are Fourier transform infrared (FT-IR) and ultraviolet differential optical absorption spectroscopy (UV-DOAS). The similarity of this technology to other assessment technologies is that air monitoring for the VOC concentration is conducted on the fenceline. The difference is that the air monitoring is conducted along a transect that, if properly arranged, can provide comprehensive monitoring. Further, monitoring is conducted as a path-integrated collection, allowing total plume capture provided that the transect is properly laid. The other advantage of using this instrumental technique is that a large amount of near real-time data can be collected, so that an emission assessment using these data can yield representative emission rate estimates (Hudson et al., 1991). Other than those limitations inherent to this class of assessment technology (meteorological effects, upwind interferences, low ambient concentrations, and required dispersion modeling), the primary disadvantage of using optical remote sensing with an air monitoring technology is the instrumental response.

Table 5-6 lists the compounds monitored and the respective nominal

TABLE 5-5. Systems being used for open-air remote sensing.

System	Typical Detection Limits (ppm × m)*	Principle of Operation
FT-IR	1.5–50	Collects full IR spectrum using broadband source and analyzes spectrum for constituents and concentrations using library spectra.
UV-DOAS	0.2–10	Collects UV spectrum over limited spectral region and measures differential absorption of line centers relative to line wings to deduce gases present and their concentrations.
GFC	5–100	Uses a sample of the gas(es) to be detected as a spectral filter and measures the broadband correlation between its spectrum and that of the measurement path to evaluate gas(es) and their concentrations.
Filtered band-pass absorption	5–100	Simple band-pass filtered absorption measurement using in- and out-band channels to measure absorption in the band of the gas(es) of interest and their concentrations.
Laser absorption	2–50	Straightforward laser transmissometry over homogeneous paths using one or more lasers to look in and out of absorption bands to deduce total monochromatic absorption and, consequently, gas concentration.
Photoacoustic spectroscopy	Absorption coefficients to 10^{-4}–10^{-6} km^{-1}	Measures the pressure rise in a closed chamber arising from collisional deactivation of excited molecules, typically carried out in an acoustic chamber to measure response acoustically and after excitation with laser source.
Lidar	1–50	Measures molecular or aerosol backscatter using either differential absorption with two wavelengths or Raman scattering to identify and measure gas concentrations; unlike other methods, provides ranging information on measurements.
Dipole-laser spectroscopy	To be determined	Developing technology for open-air use. Measures modulation caused by spectrally scanning across a line feature of the gas(es) of interest to identify and deduce concentrations by line-depth absorption.

* Detection limits are highly species-dependent because of the large variation in absorption strengths. Numbers shown are typical ranges for absorbers of moderate strength and moderate interference.

Reference: Spellicy, Crow and Davies, 1991.

TABLE 5-6.   Nominal detection limits of compounds monitored with IR and UV open-path sensors.

Compound	Detection Limits (ppm × m)*	
	IR	UV
CO	7	
NO	4	0.8
N_2O	5	
NO_2		0.3
SO_2	5	0.2
O_3	2	0.8
NH_3	1.5	1.0
CH_4	15	
C_2H_4	2	
C_3H_6	7.5	
H_2CO	3	0.3
CH_3OH	2.5	
MTBE	1.5	
1,3-Butadiene	5	
Benzene		0.75
Toluene		0.75
m-Xylene	10	0.75
p-Xylene	45	0.75
HCl	2	
CH_3Cl	10	
Cylcohexane	45	

* IR detection limits are those observed for a specific open-air test. Better limits are possible in multipass cells and under laboratory conditions. UV detection limits are values quoted by Opsis, Inc. and converted to appropriate units.
Reference: Spelicy, Crow and Davies, 1991.

detection limits using FT-IR and UV. Unfortunately, optical remote sensing now is limited to about 20 or 30 VOCs, and detection limits are equivalently higher as compared to other air monitoring techniques. As the compound response to additional VOCs and detection limits improves, so will the application of this technology for estimating VOC emission rates.

SAMPLE COLLECTION TECHNIQUE AND ANALYTICAL METHODOLOGY

As discussed earlier, most emission assessment technologies employ sample collection techniques and analytical methodologies, the selection of which will depend on the assessment technology used, the type and level of VOCs emitted, and the capabilities available to conduct the emission assessment (Radian, 1987; Riggin, 1983).

Sample collection techniques include grab sample techniques and integrated sample collection techniques. Grab sampling involves collection of the sample gas rapidly without concern for time-weighted emissions. An example of a grab sampling technique and application is whole-air sampling for VOCs, such as evacuated canisters used with a surface flux chamber. The emission sample is collected after equilibrium is attained in the chamber by affixing the canister to the exhaust of the chamber and opening the canister valve.

Grab sampling commonly is used with direct emission measurement technologies, whereas integrated sample collection usually is used with indirect assessment technologies and air monitoring/modeling technologies. Integrated sampling allows for the constant-flow collection of a gas sample into or on a medium over a specified time interval. When used with the appropriate emission assessment technology, this permits an assessment of the emission rate over time. One advantage of integrated sample collection is that the detection limit of the technique usually is improved by concentrating the VOC in a sorbing medium.

The selection of the sample collection technique will depend on many factors, including the emission assessment technology, required sensitivity, analytical methodology, and capabilities and resources available to conduct the emission assessment. Whole air sample collection using stainless steel canisters and Tedlar bags is common for direct technologies, and solid sorbents, in particular Tenax, XAD-2 resin, and activated charcoal, share common use in indirect emission assessment technologies.

The choice of analytical methodology is somewhat dependent on the same factors that affect the selection of a sampling technology, but most VOC analytical methods employ gas chromatography (GC) and hydrocarbon detectors. The GC separates the components in the gas sample to allow for identification and quantitation of VOCs although total hydrocarbon (THC) or total nonmethane hydrocarbon (TNMHC) analysis is useful and often the best "parameter" for emission assessment. The choice of a method involves selecting the most appropriate separation technique (column, temperature, eluent, flow rate) and detector. One popular method is mass spectrometer (MS) detection, which provides low-level detection and species identification with high certainty. Some detectors that are available for use respond better to groups of VOCs and offer improved detection limits as compared to MS. However, the choice of analytical methodology will not depend solely on the lower limit of detection.

DISCUSSION

In selecting an emission assessment approach, the use of an accurate and precise technology is desirable to allow the generation of representative emission estimates. The selection of an assessment approach, an assessment technology, and then a sample collection technique and analytical methodology will depend on many factors, the most important of which include: type of emission source (point or area source); type and level of VOCs emitted from the source; other source characteristics such as heterogeneity and dynamic properties, accessibility, surrounding interfering sources, and meteorological conditions; and the capabilities available to conduct the emission assessment, such as investigator expertise, equipment, and laboratory facilities.

When possible, direct emission measurement technologies, such as the emission isolation flux chamber, should be used to measure emission rates from waste bodies because they offer inherently greater sensitivity and lower variability than indirect measurements. The flux chamber is not well suited to measuring emissions from large waste bodies, areas of varied composition (with large spacial variability), or highly agitated/dynamic surfaces; but optical remote sensing can be used for these more challenging sources. In using a vent sampling technology for processes, consideration must be given to how the necessary velocity (volumetric flow rate) measurement will be made.

For VOC emission sources where direct emission measurement technologies including optical remote sensing are not appropriate, indirect emission measurement techniques, such as the concentration-profile technology or the transect technique, are preferred. A decision to use one or the other technology must, however, be based on the type of area source, environmental factors, and so on. The mass balance technology suffers from the fact that the emissions (losses) typically are small. Thus, the difference between two large values typically will have a large variability. Whenever possible, the mass balance technology should not be used as the sole means for determining an emission rate from an area source.

Air monitoring technologies can provide area source emissions data. However, these estimates may be of limited accuracy and precision for meteorological and site reasons. Often these fenceline air monitoring programs can provide useful data that satisfy other assessment needs, and optical remote sensing used as an indirect or air monitoring technique at the fenceline can enhance these assessment approaches.

REFERENCES

Astle, A. D., R. A. Duffee, and A. R. Stankunas, 1982. Estimating Vapor and Odor Emission Rates from Hazardous Waste Sites. National Conference on Management of Uncontrolled Hazardous Waste Sites, U.S. EPA, Washington, D.C.

Balfour, W. D., C. E. Schmidt, and B. M. Eklund, 1984. Sampling Approaches for Measuring Emission Rates from Hazardous Waste Disposal Facilities, Presented at the Air and Waste Management Association National Meeting, June 1984, 84-3.3.

Balfour, W. D., R. G. Weatherold, and D. L. Lewis, 1984. Evaluation of Air Emissions from Hazardous Waste Treatment, Storage, and Disposal Facilities, EPA 600/2-85/057, 2 Vols. U.S. EPA, Cincinnati, OH.

Bath, R. J., et al., 1989. Remote Sensing of Air Toxics Using State-of-the-Art Techniques, *Proceedings* of the 1989 EPA/AWMA Symposium on Measurement of Toxic and Related Air Pollutants, Raleigh, NC.

Batterman, S., B. McQuown, and A. McFarland, 1991. A Passive Soil Gas Flux Sampler: Laboratory and Field Evaluation, 84th Annual Meeting Air and Waste Management Association, Vancouver, B.C.

Berry, R. S., C. E. Schmidt, and R. C. Wells, 1991. An Evaluation of Sampling Strategies for Determining Soil Filter Control Efficiencies. Presented at the 1991 AWMA Symposium, 91-17.4, Vancouver, B.C.

Cowherd, C., 1985. Measurement of Particulate Emissions from Hazardous Waste Disposal Sites, 78th Annual Meeting Air Pollution Control Association, Detroit, MI.

DuPont, R. R., 1987. Measurement of Volatile Hazardous Organic Emissions. *J. Air Pollut. Control Assoc.*, Vol. 37, No. 3, p. 168.

Eklund, B. M., W. D. Balfour, and C. E. Schmidt, 1985. Measurement of Fugitive Volatile Organic Emission Rates. *Environ. Progr.*, Vol. 4, No. 3, p. 199.

Eklund, B. M., M. R. Keinbusch, D. Ranum, and T. Harrison, 1987. Development of a Sampling Method for Measuring VOC Emissions from Surface Impoundments. Radian Corporation, Austin, TX, 7 pp.

Eklund, B. M., M. R. Keinbusch, D. Ranum, and T. Harrison, 1987. Development of a Sampling Method for Measuring VOC Emissions from Surface Impoundments. Radian Corporation, Austin, TX.

Esplin, G. J., 1988. Boundary Layer Emissions Monitoring. *JAPCA*, Vol. 38, No. 9, pp. 1158–1161.

Farmer, W. J., M. S. Yang, J. Lety, and W. F. Spencer, 1980. Land Disposal of Hexachlorobenzene Waste: Controlling Vapor Movement in Soil, EPA 600/280-119. U.S. EPA, Cincinnati, OH.

Gholson, A. R., J. R. Albritton, K. M. Jayanty, and J. E. Knoll, 1988. Evaluation of the Flux Chamber Method for Measuring Volatile Organic Emissions from Surface Impoundments, Final Report for U.S. EPA Contract No. 68-02-4550.

Hudson, J., et al., 1991. Remote Sensing of Toxic Air Pollutants at a High Risk Point Source Using Long Path FTIR, 84th Air and Waste Management Association Annual Meeting, Vancouver, B.C.

Hwang, S. T., 1982. Measuring Rates of Volatile Emissions from Non-Point Source Hazardous Waste Facilities, 75th Annual Meeting Air Pollution Control Association, New Orleans, LA.

Hwang, S. T., 1985. Model Prediction of Volatile Emissions. *Environ. Progr.*, Vol. 4, No. 2, p. 141.

Kapling, E. J., A. J. Kurtz, and M. Rahimi, 1986. VOC Sampling for Emission Rate Determination and Ambient Air Quality on an Inactive Landfill, New England Section, Air Pollution Control Association, Fall 1986 Conference, Worcester, MA.

Kerfoot, H. B., 1987. Soil-Gas Measurement for Detection of Ground-Water Contamination by Volatile Organic Compounds. *Environ. Sci. Technol.*, Vol. 21, No. 10, p. 1002.

Lodge, J. P., Editor, 1989. *Methods of Air Sampling and Analysis,* third edition. Lewis Publisher, Inc., Chelsea, MI.

McLaren, S. E., and D. H. Stedman, 1990. Flux Measurements Using Simultaneous Long Path Ultraviolet and Infrared Spectroscopy, 83rd Annual Meeting Air and Waste Management Association, Pittsburgh, PA.

Radian Corporation, 1986. Measurement of Gaseous Emission Rates from Land Surfaces Using an Emission Isolation Flux Chamber, User's Guide, EPA Contract No. 68-02-3889.

Radian Corporation, 1987. Air Quality Engineering Manual for Hazardous Waste Site Mitigation Activities, Revision 2. Air Quality Engineering and Technology, Department of Environmental Quality CN027. (*Note:* List of compounds comes from a draft EPA communique.)

Riggin, R. M., 1983. Technical Assistance Document for Sampling and Analysis of Toxic Organic Compounds in Ambient Air, EPA-600/4-83-027. U.S. EPA, Research Triangle Park, NC.

Riggin, R. M., and W. T. Winberry, 1986. Compendium of Methods for the Determination of Toxic Organic Compounds in Ambient Air (Supplement to EPA-600/4-84-041), EPA-600/4-87-006. U.S. EPA, Research Triangle Park, NC.

Schmidt, C. E., and W. D. Balfour, 1983. Direct Gas Emission Measurement Techniques and the Utilization of Emissions Data from Hazardous Waste Sites, National Conference of Environmental Engineering Practice, Environmental Engineering Division ASCE.

Schmidt, C.E., and J. Clark, 1990. Use of the Surface Isolation Flux Chamber to Assess Fugitive Emissions from a Fixed-Roof on an Oil–Water Separator Facility. Presented at the 1990 EPA/AWMA Measurement of Air Toxics, Raleigh, NC.

Schmidt, C. E., and W. R. Faught, 1990. Review of Direct and Indirect Emission Measurement Technologies for Measuring Fugitive Emissions from Waste Water Treatment Facilities, American Institute of Chemical Engineers Symposium, San Diego, CA.

Schmidt, C. E., W. R. Faught, and J. Nottoli, 1991. Using the EPA Recommended Surface Emission Isolation Flux Chamber to Assess Emissions from Aerated and Non-aerated Liquid Surfaces. Presented at the 1991 EPA/AWMA Measurement of Air Toxics, Raleigh, NC.

Schmidt, C. E., R. Vandervort, and W. D. Balfour, 1986. Technical Approach and Sampling Techniques Used to Detect and Map Subsurface Hydrocarbon Contamination, 79th Annual Meeting Air Pollution Control Association, Minneapolis, MN.

Scotto, R. L., T. R. Minnich, and M. R. Leo, 1990. Emissions Estimation and Dispersion Analysis Using Path-Integrated Air Measurement Data from Hazardous Waste Sites, 83rd Annual Meeting Air and Waste Management Association, Pittsburgh, PA.

Spellicy, R. L., W. L. Crow, J. A. Draves, et al., 1991. Spectroscopic Remote Sensing: Addressing Requirements of the Clean Air Act. *Spectroscopy*, Vol. 6, No. 9, p. 24.

Thibodeaux, L. G., D. G. Parker, and M. M. Heck, 1982. Measurements of Volatile Chemical Emissions from Wastewater Basins. Hazardous Waste Engineering Research Laboratory, EPA 600/5-2-82/095. U.S. EPA, Cincinnati, OH.

U.S. Environmental Protection Agency, 1983. Technical Assistance Document for Sampling and Analysis of Toxic Organic Compounds in Ambient Air, EPA-600/4-83-027. Environmental Monitoring Systems Laboratory, Research Triangle Park, NC.

U.S. Environmental Protection Agency, 1989. Office of Air Quality Planning and Standards, Air Superfund National Technical Guidance Study Series, Vol. 1: Application of Air Pathway Analysis for Superfund Activities, Interim Final, EPA-450/1-89/001.

U.S. Environmental Protection Agency, 1989. Office of Air Quality Planning and Standards, Air Superfund National Technical Guidance Study Series, Vol. 2: Estimation of Baseline Air Emissions at Superfund Sites, Interim Final, EPA-450/1-89/002.

U.S. Environmental Protection Agency, 1989. Office of Air Quality Planning and Standards, Air Superfund National Technical Guidance Study Series, Vol. 3: Estimation of Air Emissions from Cleanup Activities at Superfund Sites, Interim Final, EPA-450/1-89/003.

U.S. Environmental Protection Agency, 1989. Office of Air Quality Planning and Standards, Air Superfund National Technical Guidance Study Series, Vol. 4: Procedures for Dispersion Modeling for Superfund Air Pathway Analysis, Interim Final, EPA-450/1-89/004.

U.S. Environmental Protection Agency, 1990. Development of a Statement-of-Work (SOW) for the Analysis of Air Toxics at Superfund Sites as Part of the Contract Laboratory Program (CLP), *Proceedings* of the 1990 EPA/AWMA International Symposium on Measurement of Toxic and Related Air Pollutants.

Whitcraft, W. K., and K. N. Wood, 1990. Use of Remote Sensing to Measure Wastewater Treatment Plant Emissions, 83rd Annual Meeting Air and Waste Management Association, Pittsburgh, PA.

Winberry, W. T., and N. Murphy, 1989. (First and Second) Supplement to Compendium of Methods for the Determination of Toxic Organic Compounds in Ambient Air, EPA-600/4-87-006 Sept. 1986 and EPA-600/4-89-018. U.S. EPA, Environmental Monitoring Systems, Research Triangle Park, NC.

Wisner, C. E., and T. W. Davis, 1989. Characterization of Fugitive Emission Rates Using a Mobile Integrating Sampler, *Proceedings* of the 1989 EPA/ AWMA Symposium on Measurement of Toxic and Related Air Pollutants, Raleigh, NC.

Wood, J. A., and M. L. Porter, 1986. Hazardous Pollutants in Class II Landfills, South Coast Air Quality Management District, El Monte, CA.

6

Mathematical Models

Some of the best methods for obtaining VOC emission rate data are measurement technologies that include direct and indirect measurement or air monitoring of ambient concentrations and model estimates of emission rates. However, implementing these approaches to obtain emission rate data is not always possible for a variety of reasons, such as project resource limitations, restricted capabilities, and specific site constraints. All assessment techniques have advantages and disadvantages or limitations, and some approaches may not be appropriate for certain applications.

Usually, measurement approaches such as direct measurement techniques and ambient air monitoring approaches are conducted at a few specific test locations chosen to be representative of a much larger area. In addition, the results of a short-term direct measurement program usually are extrapolated to determine the emissions over a much longer time period. Many factors can vary over such an extended period, including meteorological conditions, source strength, and operational variables. If the source is such that the variations will significantly affect the emission rate, then either a much more comprehensive direct measurement program is required, or some way of extrapolating the direct measurement data accurately must be developed.

Mathematical models allow investigators to screen sites for emissions potential and to make preliminary emissions measurements, and to accurately extrapolate resource-intensive direct measurement data. The mathematical models, or fate expressions, for emission rate assessment and air quality assessment are described as statistical models, predictive emission models, and atmospheric dispersion models. As with any modeling, care must be taken to obtain useful data. The proper use of models to estimate the VOC emission rate includes proper model selection, developing a representative physical emission scenario, translating that scenario into the model, and collecting and using a representative model input. These considerations must be addressed in order to generate a useful, representative output.

Statistical models relate VOC emissions to air quality on the basis of an analysis of ambient air quality monitoring data. The simplest statistical model assumes that the present air quality (VOC ambient concentration) can be linearly scaled in direct proportion to VOC emissions. Statistical models are well developed and are not discussed further in this book.

Predictive emissions models were developed for specific physical situations or treatment processes. The input for these models varies, but it always includes input related to the VOC source strength term, such as the chemical composition and the concentration. This serves as the driving force in the model. The structure or the principles of the emission process are described for the specific model, and the remaining input required to operate the model usually involves the emission event, such as migration of a VOC through a porous medium or across a physical barrier or interface such as a liquid–air interface. Often it is these physical data that are difficult to obtain, and which have a significant influence on the estimated VOC emission rate. The advantage of predictive models is that if these input data are known with confidence, and the model used represents the physical situation, then useful estimates can be obtained for a variety of conditions (e.g., summer and winter conditions). Limitations, however, include nonrepresentative models and model input, resulting in data of unknown quality, inaccurate VOC emission estimates, and limited data utility. The following presentation of predictive models describes models applicable to a variety of waste treatment processes/dispositions, all of them capable, when used properly, of generating at least screening-level VOC emission rate data.

Atmospheric dispersion models are well developed and are used to describe the transport and transformation of air pollutants through the atmosphere. Dispersion modeling typically is used to predict the impact from an emission event on a downwind receptor. This is the common application for health risk assessment. There are a variety of models for this purpose, the most popular of which will be discussed. Dispersion modeling also can be used to estimate VOC emission rates if ambient concentrations and representative meteorological data are available. This is done by allowing the model to simulate the transport conditions during the ambient monitoring and then inserting an assumed emission rate into the model. The modeled ambient concentration then is compared to the measured concentration, and the assumed emission rate is adjusted and iteratively remodeled. In this way, ambient data and a dispersion model can be used to estimate VOC emissions without measurement of emission rates in the field.

PREDICTIVE EMISSION MODELS

Predictive emission models have been developed by scientific and engineering researchers to predict emission rates for a variety of waste site types, and have been used in recent years to predict emission rates from hazardous waste treatment and disposal sites such as surface impoundments and landfills. These models are based on diffusion/partition theory, and the emission rates are calculated by determining the mass transfer coefficient or partition of the chemical or chemical compound of interest. Because of a variety of waste site and waste properties, it is essential to understand the assumptions of each model and the sensitivity of each variable in the model, as well as the waste form and characteristics. Detailed descriptions of each model and their derivations can be found in the references (Arnold, 1944; Cohen et al., 1978; Farmer et al., 1980; Freeman, 1979; Hwang, 1982; MacKay and Leinonen, 1975; Owen et al., 1964; RTI, 1987; Shen 1982 a, b, 1984; Shen et al., 1985; Smith and Bomberger, 1980; Thibodeaux, 1981; Tofflemire and Shen, 1979).

All models are based on diffusion theory and mass transfer principles, but there are differences in the methods employed to calculate the individual mass transfer coefficients and the basic assumptions between models. These models are almost exclusively theoretical, and each model generally applies only to a specific type of waste site. Only limited data are available to validate those available emission predictive models, and further validation research is critically needed for investigators to have confidence in the model applications.

Many of the air emission models available for area source emission estimates are listed in Table 6-1, along with information on their application and additional references. It is important that the user understand the advantages and the disadvantages of the predictive models selected and the input requirements of these models. Detailed guidance documents on air quality models and air emission standards for TSDF permit application and permit review have been published by the U.S. EPA's Office of Air Quality and Permitting Standards (U.S. EPA, 1986, 1987, 1989).

Emission models require site and waste characterization data, which

TABLE 6-1.   Listing of predictive models for estimating emissions for area sources.*

Predictive Model	Application	Comment
Farmer original	Covered landfill	Developed for hexachloroben-zene waste
Farmer modified	Covered landfill	Modification of Farmer model to include porosity term
Shen (Farmer)	Covered landfill	Simplification of Farmer model, some oversimplifica-tion
Hwang (Farmer)	Covered landfill	Modifications of Shen model to correct oversimplification
Farmer as modified by Shen and Hwang	Covered landfill with codis-posal	Includes factor for biogas generation at codisposal sites
Thibodeaux	Covered landfill	Two-film resistance theory model
	Covered landfill with codis-posal	Accounts for biogas flow through soil
	Covered landfill with codis-posal and barometric pumping	Includes effects of changes in barometric pressure
RTI closed landfill	Covered landfill	Based on Farmer model; accounts for barometric pumping and decline in emission rate with time
RTI land treatment	Open landfills, waste pile, land treatment	Applicable to waste mixed with soil
Arnold, modified by Ziegler	Open landfills	Includes wind speed variable
RTI open dump	Open landfills	Derived from Arnold model for spills; applicable to uncovered waste
MacKay–Leinonen	Nonaerated surface impound-ment	Non-steady-state model based on two-film resistance theory
Thibodeaux, Parker, and Heck	Aerated and nonaerated surface impoundment	Based on two-film resistance theory
Smith, Bomberger, and Haynes	Nonaerated surface impound-ment	For highly volatile species only

* This table is not inclusive of all available predictive emission models.

may be available from previous investigations. Waste characterization data can also be obtained or can be assumed with some level of confidence. These data serve as the "driving force" for predictive emission rate modeling. Model input data such as site-specific data, literature values, or assumed values should be based on the requirements of the decision-making process and the available level of effort and resources. Site-specific data should be used whenever possible to increase the accuracy of the emission rate estimates. The most important parameters required to implement the predictive emission models are the waste composition, the diffusion/partition coefficients, and the meteorological conditions.

The emission rate potential (ERP) of volatile organic compounds (VOCs) from waste treatment and disposal sites is waste-dependent and site-specific. Predictive emission models described in this chapter include those of landfill sites and surface impoundments. Landfill sites contain chemical compounds in various forms (e.g., solids or liquids, bulk solids, adsorbed bulk, sludge, and contaminated soil). These sites may be covered with soils or without a cover. The selection of an emission-predictive model for air quality assessment depends mainly upon the waste form or disposition and site conditions.

The landfill models are divided into two groups: covered and uncovered landfills. The uncovered landfills may subdivided into two types based on the form of the waste: solid, sludge or contaminated soil. They provide representative estimates of area source emissions from waste treatment and disposal facilities. The surface impoundment model without mechanical agitation will be discussed. The state-of-the-art models that may be used for estimating VOC emissions from landfills and surface impoundments are presented below.

EPA has provided guidance on air emissions models specific to predicting air emissions from TSDFs (EPA 1989). This guidance includes a discussion of the air emission pathways, the importance of understanding these pathways, a description of available predictive models, and data showing how predicted emission rate data obtained by the use of these models, compare to field test data. The categories of air emission models presented in this guidance document is given in Table 6-2.

Landfills with Cover

Within a soil matrix, diffusion of a gas is affected by the size and the arrangement of interconnected voids or pores created by the soil particles. Increases in soil moisture will increase the length of the diffusion path and decrease the dry pore volume available for gas diffusion. Thus, mass transfer within soils can be described in terms of an effective diffusion coefficient, D_{ei}, which is a function of the air-filled porosity, the soil particle geometry, and the soil moisture content.

The emission rate of volatile organic compounds from a covered site can be estimated by the following mathematical expression:

$$(ERP)_i = \frac{D_{ei} C_{si} A W_i}{L} \tag{6-1}$$

defining

$$D_{ei} = \frac{D_i P_a^{10/3}}{P_t^2} \tag{6-2}$$

TABLE 6-2.   Summary of HWDF air emission models available from EPA (USEPA 1989).

- Surface Impoundments/Open Tanks
  - Quiescent surfaces with flow
  - Mechanically aerated impoundments—aerated sludge units
  - Disposal impoundments with quiescent surfaces
  - Diffused air systems
  - Oil film surfaces
- Land Treatment
  - Land treatment
  - Waste application
  - Oil film
- Landfills and Waste Piles
  - Closed landfills
  - Fixation pits
  - Open landfills and waste piles
- Transfer, Storage, and Handling Operations
  - Container loading
  - Container storage
  - Container cleaning
  - Stationary tank loading
  - Stationary tank storage
  - Spills
  - Fugitive emissions
  - Vacuum truck loading

(Reference: U.S. EPA 6-2)

$$P_a = P_t - \frac{G_{sw}d_b}{d_w} \tag{6-3}$$

$$P_t = 1 - \frac{d_b}{d_p} \tag{6-4}$$

$$C_{si} = \frac{p_i M_i}{RT} \tag{6-5}$$

where:

$(ERP)_i$ = emission rate potential of compound i in the waste (g/sec)
D_{ei} = effective diffusion coefficient of compound i (cm²/sec)
D_i = diffusion coefficient of compound i (cm²/sec)
C_{si} = saturated vapor concentration (g/cm³)
p_i = vapor pressure of compound i (mm Hg)
M_i = molecular weight of compound i (g/mol)
R = molar gas constant (62.3 mm Hg-1/°K-mol)
T = absolute temperature (°K)

A = exposed area (cm²)
P_t = soil total porosity (cm³/cm³)
P_a = soil air-filled porosity (cm³/cm³)
G_{sw} = gravimetric soil water content (g/g)
W_i = weight fraction of compound i (g/g)
L = effective depth of soil cover (cm)
d_b = soil bulk density (g/cm³)
d_p = soil particle density (g/cm³)
d_w = water density (g/cm³)

In general, the particle density of most soil is about 2.65 g/cm³. The soil bulk density is a function of the water content of the soil and the air-filled porosity. It varies between 1.0 and 2.0 g/cm³. If the soil is assumed to be dry and has a bulk density of 1.2 g/cm³, the soil porosity would be 0.55 and $G_{sw} = 0$, which represents a maximum volatilization rate. If the soil is assumed to be compacted, or has a high moisture content, its porosity may decrease to 0.35. When the soil is dry and loose and $G_{sw} = 0$ ($P_a = P_t$), the effective diffusion coefficient $D_{ei} = D_i P_t^{4/3}$ and $(ERP)_i$ becomes:

$$(ERP)_i = \frac{D_i C_{si} A P_t^{4/3} W_i}{L} \qquad (6\text{-}6)$$

Landfills without Cover (Open Dump)

Two different cases are evaluated. In the first case the waste is mostly solid; in the second the waste is a sludge or otherwise saturated with moisture.

Where the waste is in the form of a solid:

$$(ERP)_i = 2C_{si}W_iW \sqrt{\frac{D_iLv}{\pi F_v t}} \qquad (6\text{-}7)$$

where:
$(ERP)_i$ = emission rate potential of compound i in the waste (g/sec)
C_{si} = saturated vapor concentration of compound i (g/sec)
W = width of site (cm)
W_i = weight fraction of compound i in the waste (g/g)
L = length of the site parallel to the wind direction (cm)
D_i = diffusion coefficient of compound i (cm²/sec)
v = wind speed (cm/sec)
F_v = correction factor (see Figure 6-1)
t = time (sec)

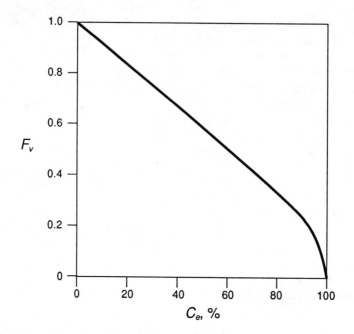

FIGURE 6-1.   Correction factor, F_v, plotted against equivalent vapor, C_e. (*Data source:* Arnold, 1944)

Where the waste is in the form of a sludge (or otherwise saturated):

$$(ERP)_i = \frac{H_c}{K_{sw}} \cdot \frac{2AD_{ei}W_i}{\sqrt{\pi\beta t}} \tag{6-8}$$

defining

$$\beta = \frac{D_{ei}}{P_t + d_p(1 - P_t)\dfrac{K_{sw}}{H_c}} \tag{6-9}$$

$$D_{ei} = D_i P_t^{4/3} \tag{6-10}$$

where:

    H = Henry's law constant
    A = exposed area (cm²)
    K_{sw} = soil/water partition coefficient

K_{sw}/H = partition coefficient for a compound between the air and soil phases

D_{ei} = effective diffusion coefficient of compound i (cm²/sec)

W_i = weight fraction (g/g)

D_i = diffusion coefficient of compound i (cm²/sec)

P_t = soil porosity

d_p = soil particle density (g/cm³)

t = time (sec)

In general, the solubility and the vapor pressure of organic compounds vary with the molecular weight and the chlorine content. VOCs with more chlorine and higher molecular weights are generally less soluble and have lower vapor pressures than VOCs with less chlorine and lower molecular weights. Thus, the environmental behavior of VOCs is expected to vary by the degree of chlorination and the molecular weight. In the analysis of potential emissions from land disposal sites, average weight fractions or concentrations of concerned compounds may be used.

Surface Impoundments

Using a two-film diffusion model (Liss and Slater, 1974) the rate of organic compound volatilization from a surface impoundment can be calculated by the following equation:

$$(ERP)_i = (18 \times 10^{-6})K_{OAi}AC_i \tag{6-11}$$

where:

$(ERP)_i$ = emission rate of compound i (g/sec)

K_{OAi} = overall mass transfer coefficient of compound i (g-mol/cm²-sec)

A = surface area of the surface impoundment (cm²)

C_i = dissolved organic concentration in water of compound i (mg/l or mg/kg)

The overall mass transfer coefficient, K_{OAi}, can be calculated from the two-resistance theory of mass transfer as follows:

$$K_{OAi} = \cfrac{1}{\cfrac{1}{K_{Li}} + \cfrac{1}{K_i K_{Gi}}} \tag{6-12}$$

where:

K_{Li} = liquid-phase mass-transfer coefficient of compound i (g-mol/cm²-sec)

K_{Gi} = gas-phase mass-transfer coefficient of compound i (g-mol/cm²-sec)

K_i = equilibrium constant of liquid and gas phase of compound i (dimensionless)

The quantity K_i can be determined from the Henry's constants, H_i, which are the ratio of bulk concentrations in air and water at equilibrium. For practical use, these constants must be adjusted for the molecular weight, temperature, liquid molar density, and gas molar density:

$$K_i = \frac{H_i}{RT} \left(\frac{C_L}{C_G} \right) \tag{6-13}$$

where:

H_i = Henry's law constant for compound i (atm-m³/mol)

R = gas constant (8.2×10^{-5} m³-atm/mol-°K)

T = temperature (°K)

C_L = liquid molar density (g-mol/m³)

C_G = gas molar density (g-mol/m³)

The determination of K_i from the Henry's law constants is valid for the condition of dilute aqueous solutions of sparingly soluble compounds. In addition, determining which phase will control the overall mass transfer has been theoretically shown, and experimentally confirmed, to be a function of the value of H_i. The following phase-controlling conditions have been suggested:

- Liquid-phase control, $K_i = K_L$, where $H_i > 10^{-3}$.
- Gas-phase control, $K_i = K_G$, when $H_i < 2 \times 10^{-5}$.
- Both phases contribute to the mass transfer rate, $2 \times 10^{-5} < H_i < 10^{-3}$.

The value of K_{Li} depends on the degree of turbulence that exists at and below the water surface, the presence of surface materials, and the meteorological conditions occurring at the gas–liquid interface, which may vary with time. K_{Li} and K_{Gi} can be calculated by the following equations:

$$K_{Li} = 4.45 \times 10^{-3} M_i^{-0.5} 1.024^{(t-20)} U_s^{0.67} H^{-0.85} \tag{6-14}$$

where:

M_i = compound i molecular weight (g/g-mol)

t = temperature (°C)

U_s = surface velocity equal to 0.015 times the wind velocity (m/sec)
H = depth of the surface impoundment (cm)

and:

$$K_{Gi} = 8.05 \times 10^{-4}M_i^{-1}U^{0.78}Z^{-0.11}S_c^{-0.67} \qquad (6\text{-}15)$$

defining

$$Z = \sqrt{\frac{4A}{2\pi}}$$

where:
U = wind speed (m/hr)
S_c = gas-phase Schmidt number
Z = effective diameter of the surface impoundment (m)
A = site area (m^2)

Emission rates should be calculated for wind speeds ranging from 1 to 10 m/sec. The surface areas of the surface impoundments and the water depth, H, must be measured on-site. A value of $S_c^{-0.67}$ equal to 0.5 may be used for high molecular weight compounds. The dissolved organic concentrations, C_i, for 20°C along with Henry's constants, H_i, for 25°C in the analyses must be calculated in μg/l.

Average Emission Rate Conversion

The result of an emission rate prediction from all models is instantaneous and commonly is expressed in g/sec, which may be converted to values for other time periods such as hourly averages or daily average emission rates as follows:

$$E_2 = E_1 \sqrt{\frac{T_2}{T_1}} \qquad (6\text{-}16)$$

where the subscript 1 denotes the average emission rate in g/sec, and subscript 2 denotes the value of the average emission rate during the desired time period, T_2, in g/hr, g/day, or g/yr. For example, an hourly emission rate would be:

$$E_{g/hr} = E_{g/sec} \sqrt{3,600 \text{ sec/hr}} = 60 \text{ hr} \times E_{g/sec} \qquad (6\text{-}17)$$

To convert the g/sec emission rate to a daily emission rate:

$$E_{g/day} = E_{g/sec} \sqrt{86,400 \text{ sec/day}} = 294 \text{ day} \times E_{g/sec} \qquad (6\text{-}18)$$

Illustrative Examples

Example 1

An open dump site has industrial wastes containing 5,000 ppm by weight of PCBs as Aroclor 1242 in soil. The site is of irregular shape; its longest cross dimension is 300 m, and its shortest cross dimension is approximately 180 m with an exposure area of about 35,000 m². The potential emission rate of PCBs from the site is to be estimated, assuming a wind speed of 4 m/sec and a soil surface temperature of 30°C.

Applying the equation:

$$(ERP)_i = 2C_s W_i W \sqrt{\frac{D_i L v}{\pi F_v}} \qquad (6\text{-}19)$$

defining

$$C_s = \frac{pM}{RT}$$

where:

$p = 4 \times 10^{-3}$ mm Hg
$M = 258$ g/mol
$R = 62.3$ mm Hg-l/°K-mol
$T = 273 + 30 = 303$°K
$C_s = 4 \times 10^{-3} \times 258/(62,300 \times 303) = 5.5 \times 10^{-8}$ g/cm³
$W_i = 0.005$
$W = 18,000$ cm
$L = 30,000$ cm (the longest dimension)
$D_i = 0.0519$ cm²/sec at 30°C
$v = 400$ cm/sec
$F_v = 1$ (from Figure 6-1)

yielding:

$$(ERP)_i = 2 \times (5.5 \times 10^{-8}) \times 0.005 \times 30,000 \sqrt{\frac{0.0519 \times 18,000 \times 400}{3.14159 \times 1}}$$

$$= 0.005678 \text{ g/sec } (5,678 \text{ } \mu\text{g/sec})$$

Example 2

If the site, as described in Example 1, is covered with 20 inches of soil with a total porosity of 0.4, what will be the potential emission rate of PCBs?

Applying the equation:

$$(ERP)_i = \frac{D_i C_s A P_t^{4/3}}{L} \qquad (6\text{-}20)$$

where:

$D_i = 0.0519$ cm²/sec
$C_s = pM/(RT) = 4 \times 10^{-3} \times 258/(62,300 \times 303) = 5.5 \times 10^{-8}$ g/mol
$A = 35,000$ m² $= 3.5 \times 10^8$ cm²
$P_t = 0.4$
$L = 20 \times 2.54 = 50.8$ cm

yielding:

$$(ERP)_i = \frac{0.0159 \times (5.5 \times 10^{-8}) \times (3.5 \times 10^8) \times (0.4)^{4/3}}{50.8}$$

$$= 0.0000346 \text{ g/sec } (34.6 \ \mu\text{g/sec})$$

Example 3

It is necessary to estimate daily PCB 1254 emissions from the surface of a 1,000 m² site where contaminated river sediments were dumped before the site was covered with soil. The average concentration of PCB 1254 in the sediments was given as 1,000 ppm by weight, the soil porosity is 0.35, and the density of the soil is 2.65 g/cm³.

Applying the equation:

$$(ERP)_i = \frac{H_c}{K_{sw}} \cdot \frac{2AD_{ei}W_i}{\sqrt{\pi \beta t}} \qquad (6\text{-}21)$$

defining

$$\beta = \frac{D_{ei}}{P_t + d_p(1 - P_t)\dfrac{K_{sw}}{H_i}}$$

$$D_{ei} = D_i P_t^{4/3}$$

where:

$A = 1,000$ m² $= 10^7$ cm²
$P_t = 0.35$

$$d_p = 2.65$$
$$H_c = 8.37 \times 10^{-3} \text{ atm-m}^3/\text{g-mol} = 0.343 \text{ atm-cm}^3/\text{g-mol}$$
$$K_{sw} = 1,000$$
$$D_i = 0.05 \text{ cm}^2/\text{sec}$$
$$W_i = 1,000 \text{ ppm}$$
$$t = 1 \text{ day} = 86,400 \text{ sec}$$

yielding:

$$D_{ei} = D_i P_t^{4/3} = 0.05 \times (0.35)^{4/3} = 0.01232 \text{ cm}^2/\text{sec}$$

$$\beta = \frac{0.01232}{0.35 + 2.65(0.65)\left(\dfrac{1000}{0.343}\right)} = \frac{0.01232}{5,022} = 2.45 \times 10^{-6} \text{ cm}^2/\text{sec}$$

$$\frac{H_i}{K_{sw}} = \frac{0.343}{1,000} = 3.43 \times 10^{-4}$$

$$(ERP)_i = (3.43 \times 10^{-4}) \frac{2 \times 10^7(0.01233) \times 10^{-3}}{\sqrt{3.14159 \times (2.45 \times 10^{-6}) \times 86,400}} = 0.1 \text{ g/day}$$

Example 4

A holding pond of river sediments containing PCBs has a surface area of approximately 1,000 m², with an average depth of 3 m. The average saturation concentration of PCBs in the surface water was reported to be 10 ppm as Aroclor 1254. What is the daily emission rate potential of PCBs? Assume that the wind speed is equal to 1.0 m/sec, and the water surface temperature is 25°C.

Applying the equation:

$$(ERP)_i = (18 \times 10^{-6})K_{OAi}AC_i \qquad (6\text{-}22)$$

For emissions from a lagoon or a pond, experience indicates that the liquid diffusion coefficient controls; therefore, $K_{OA} = K_L$, and

$$K_{Li} = 4.45 \times 10^{-3} M_i^{-0.5} 1.024^{(t-20)} U_s^{0.67} H^{-0.85}$$

where:
$$A = 1,000 \text{ m}^2$$
$$C_i = 100 \text{ ppm} (\approx 10 \text{ mg/l})$$
$$t = 25°C$$
$$H = 300 \text{ cm}$$
$$U = 100 \times 0.035 = 3.5 \text{ cm/sec}$$
$$M_i = 328 \text{ g/mol}$$

yielding:

$$K_{OA} = 4.45 \times 10^{-3} (328)^{-0.5} 1.024^{(25-20)} (3.5)^{0.67} (300)^{-0.85}$$

$$= 5.03 \times 10^{-6} \frac{\text{g-mol}}{\text{cm}^2\text{-sec}}$$

$$(ERP)_i = (1.8 \times 10^{-5}) \times (5.03 \times 10^{-6}) \times 10 \times 10^7 = 0.009 \text{ g/sec}$$

$$E_{\text{day}} = E_i(\text{g/sec}) \sqrt{(3,600 \times 24)\text{sec/day}} = 0.009 \times 294 = 2.646 \text{ g/day}$$

ATMOSPHERIC DISPERSION MODELS

Atmospheric dispersion models calculate ambient VOC concentrations with reasonable accuracy at various locations of the concerned receptors. Therefore, they have application as a screening mechanism for ambient air quality assessment, permit application, and determination of whether there is a health risk involved. Atmospheric dispersion models simulate the complex atmospheric processes involved in the transport and the dispersion of chemical compounds of interest. Mathematical equations are used to describe the sources and the quantities of VOC emissions, the transport of VOCs, and the removal of the organic compounds from the atmosphere.

The VOC impact associated with waste treatment emissions can be estimated through the use of dispersion models, provided that a VOC emission rate estimate is measured or calculated with predictive modeling. The simplest dispersion model, known as the box model, equates ambient concentrations to the mass of pollutants within a specified volume of the atmosphere divided by the volume. More complex dispersion models attempt to simulate mass balance within individual parcels of air. These models employ equations that simulate the various processes influencing this mass balance. Such processes include transport, turbulent diffusion, and reaction of pollutant species. The complexity of dispersion models depends upon the assumptions one is willing to make. Models may be formulated to describe the behavior of chemically reactive pollutants, or they may be limited in application to nonreactive, inert pollutants. A steady-state assumption commonly is employed in many dispersion models. The assumption means that the processes affecting the mass balance do not change with time.

A screening model may be used to estimate 1-hour ambient contributions from individual sources. This model is limited to a single-source evaluation (point or area). It can accept the input of the atmospheric stability class and the windspeed, and it requires very short run times. Its principal disadvantages are that it cannot consider multiple sources, actual meteorological data, and averaging periods other than 1 hour. Because of these disadvantages the results must be manually converted to other averaging times, and the contributions from multiple sources must be added (U.S. EPA, 1990).

A screening analysis for VOC emission/air quality impacts has been established by most governmental pollution regulatory agencies. If a specific source passes the screening analysis, then the source may be exempted from sophisticated air quality modeling to show compliance with the increments of VOC concentrations and the regulatory ambient air quality standards or guidelines. As an example, screening procedures for the calculation of annual average impacts of VOC emissions are described in the New York State Air Guide—1 document (NYSDEC, 1991), as presented below.

Screening Procedures Area Source Method

The area source method may be used to determine maximum actual annual, potential annual, and short-term impacts from an area source at a specified downwind distance. That specified downwind distance must be *outside* the area source. When there are multiple area and/or point sources, the impacts should be summed. The method proceeds as follows:

1. Determine the side length, S, of the area source, in feet. The area source should be square. The side length, S, should be greater than 30 feet but less than 3,300 feet.
2. Determine the distance, D, from the center of the area source to the desired point of impact, in feet. For most permitting applications, assume that D is equal to the distance to the property line, D_{pl}. The desired point of impact must be outside the area source. More precisely, D must be greater than the effective radius of the area source, R_e, as defined below:

$$R_e(\text{feet}) = 0.56\ S \qquad\qquad (6\text{-}23)$$

where S (feet) is the side length of the area source, defined above.
3. Determine the height, h_A, of the area source, in feet. Assume this to be the released height of the pollutant. The area source height should be less than 100 feet. For ground-level sources, assume that h_A equals 3 feet. For area source heights, h_A, greater than 3 feet, the equations below overpredict the impacts closest to the source. This conservatism is most pronounced for distances, D, less than D_{max}, where D_{max} is the approximate distance to the maximum impact for a given area

source height as defined below:

$$D_{max}(\text{feet}) = 9.84(h_A)^{1.15} \qquad (6\text{-}24)$$

where h_A is the height of the area source in feet. If D is less than D_{max}, substitute D_{max} for D in the equations below.

4. Calculate the maximum *actual annual impact*, C_a, from the area source at the desired point of impact (distance D), using the equation below:

$$C_a(\mu g/m^3) = \frac{104\ Q_a}{(D + S)^{1.6}\ h_A^{0.368}} \qquad (6\text{-}25)$$

where Q_a is the annual emission rate in lb/yr, and D, S, and h_A are as defined above.

5. Calculate the maximum *potential annual impact*, C_p, from the area source at the desired point of impact (distance D), using the equation below:

$$C_p(\mu g/m^3) = \frac{914{,}000\ Q}{(D + S)^{1.6}\ h_A^{0.368}} \qquad (6\text{-}26)$$

where Q is the hourly emission rate in lb/hr, and D, S, and h_A are as defined above.

6. Calculate the maximum *short-term impact*, C_{ST}, from the area source, using the equation below:

$$C_{ST}(\mu g/m^3) = C_p\ 100 \qquad (6\text{-}27)$$

where C_p is the maximum potential annual impact as defined above.

Alternate Area Source Method

The following alternate method for area sources was developed specifically for remediation projects and urban scale emissions. It has the flexibility to permit the calculation of the maximum annual concentration *within* an area source. Annual impacts may be estimated both within and downwind from an area source. However, the method has not been modified to estimate short-term impacts. The contribution from nearby area sources can be calculated by the procedures outlined next. Only sources located within a distance of $3S$ (S is the length of a side of the area source) from the source being analyzed need be considered. The method can calculate impacts at receptor distances from the source boundary to a distance of $2.5S$ from the area source. This range encompasses practically all cases of interest in those types of applications.

The following procedures are valid for ground-level area sources, effectively less than 10 feet in height, with side lengths greater than 330 feet:

1. Determine the area source emission rate, Q_A, in units of lb/(hr-ft^2) by dividing the total annual emission rate, Q_a (lb/hr), by the area, A (ft^2), of the source.

$$Q_A \left(\frac{\text{lb}}{\text{hr-ft}^2} \right) = \frac{(\text{emission rate})}{(\text{area})} = \frac{Q_a}{A} \qquad (6\text{-}28)$$

2. Calculate the maximum *actual annual impact*, C_a, *within* the area source as defined below:

$$C_a(\mu g/m^3) = KQ_AC_m$$

where:
   $K = 15$ for $330 \text{ ft} \le S < 3{,}300 \text{ ft}$
   $K = 30$ for $S \ge 3{,}300 \text{ ft}$
   $C_m = 1.355 \times 10^6$, a conversion factor from lb/(hr-ft^2) to $\mu g/m^2$-sec

3. If the receptors of interest are located off-site and are from one to 2.5 times the side length of the area source away, divide the concentration calculated in step (2) by the following factors:

Receptor downwind distance ($\times S$)	1	1.5	2	2.5
Concentration reduction factor	7	20	25	35

4. If there are other area sources within $3S$ distances from the source being considered (ideally contiguous to the source being analyzed), then the contribution of these sources can be determined by redefining Q_A in step (2) as:

$$Q_A = Q_{A0} + 0.32Q_{A1} + 0.18Q_{A2} + 0.13Q_{A3} \qquad (6\text{-}29)$$

where Q_{A0} represents the emissions from the source under consideration, and Q_{A1} to Q_{A3} represent emissions from sources (if they exist) that are at *upwind* distances of $1S$, $2S$, $2.5S$, and $3S$, respectively, from the Q_{A0} source. It must be noted that the nearby sources are assumed to be of about the same size as the source under consideration.

An ambient air quality impact assessment is required as part of the screening procedure. That assessment requires comparison of predicted worst-case annual and short-term impacts to the appropriate standards or guideline values. It is important to understand that the screening methods generally are conservative. This is especially true for the short-term impact hand calculation methods. When hand-calculated impacts exceed the appropriate standards or guideline values, the AG-1 software program and/or the SCREEN model should be used to reduce that conservatism. The SCREEN model should be used as the last step in the short-term impact screening procedure before a refined air quality impact analysis is initiated.

When there are multiple sources of a contaminant and a great separation between sources, the conservatism in the short-term methods may be pronounced. In such a case, summing short-term impacts may be unrealistically conservative. That level of conservatism increases with increasing variations in stack heights and source separation. Source separation become critical when it would be impossible for all sources to impact the point of maximum concentration for a given wind direction. In assessing annual impacts, the consideration of multiple sources is not so critical because wind direction varies *over a yearly period*. Therefore, because the wind direction changes, all sources generally impact the point of maximum concentration in varying degrees.

If the Air Guide—1 analysis shows that the impacts are unacceptable, it may be possible to reduce the conservatism in the above analysis. If the level of conservatism cannot be reduced, a site-specific analysis should be performed. EPA-recommended models, such as the short-term and long-term versions of the Industrial Source Complex (ISCST and ISCLT) model, should be used in the site-specific analysis.

Refined Atmospheric Dispersion Models

The above procedures allow the user to perform a first-level analysis of the expected impact from a waste treatment and disposal facility. The predicted impacts then are compared to allow ambient levels of the pollutants to be defined from a chronic-effects standpoint. The use of a site-specific analysis for VOC assessment is preferred.

Industrial source complex (ISC) models may be used to determine long-term and short-term ambient VOC concentrations. The ISC models can estimate ambient concentrations at discrete receptor sites from point sources, area sources, and line sources at a TSDF site. The ISC models may be divided into short-term and long-term models (ISCST, ISCLT). The principal advantage of the ISCST model is the large number and the types of sources that can be evaluated simultaneously to estimate an overall ambient concentration over a variety of time periods (i.e., 1-, 3-, 8-, and 24-hour averages). The disadvantage of the ISCST model is its long run-time requirements for execution. The ISCST model computes the values necessary for the annual ambient concentrations used for chronic exposure risk assessment, whereas the ISCST computes the predicted values for short-term (acute) exposure.

The preferred U.S. EPA atmospheric dispersion models and selected applications are presented in a simple format with references as shown in Appendix G. The first section contains the refined models preferred by the U.S. EPA in simple terrain. These models are intended for use with criteria pollutants from stationary sources although other applications are possible. The use of screening methods followed by a refined analysis is the preferred procedure. Detailed information on air quality models and guidelines can be found in U.S. EPA publications (U.S. EPA, 1978, 1979, 1986, 1987).

In modeling, computer techniques are extremely valuable when properly applied. Computers are able to calculate the concentration of problem contaminants in the ambient air at various distances from the emission source under varying meteorological and topographical conditions. However, any computer solution with limited input data should be considered questionable. As for computer modeling, the capabilities of the computer would far exceed the ability to obtain input data even if the way to obtain representative input data were known for most applications.

Most atmospheric dispersion models produce estimates of contaminant concentrations at selected receptor locations. The locations may be divided into a network of points on the receptor grid. Some models allow the user to choose the receptor locations. Usually, a uniform pattern, either rectangular or circular, is selected. Some models also allow the inclusion of terrain features by permitting the user to specify the height of each receptor above or below the source elevation.

The information needed for input to most models includes the source description, emission data, receptor information, and meteorological data. The source description and emission data generally are derived from the emission predictive model. The receptor information can be obtained by a field survey. The meteorological data generally include the wind direction, wind speed, atmospheric stability, and mixing height. The Gaussian model is the basic tool for dispersion calculations and is the model most commonly used. Several standard models have been developed for air quality assessment. Selecting the most suitable model means that one must evaluate the physical characteristics of the source and the surrounding area and search for a model that will best simulate those characteristics mathematically. The selection is critical because it can be expensive if one uses a model that overpredicts or underpredicts ambient concentrations of a contaminant from a specific emission source.

The use of dispersion models to assess VOC ambient concentrations in TSDF sites requires reliable input data of VOC emission rates from emission-predictive models, as discussed previously. During the last several years, the ISC dispersion models have been improved greatly through the efforts and refinements of hundreds of meteorologists. Unfortunately, only a few scientists and engineers have been devoting their time and energy to emission model research efforts to improve the available models and validate them experimentally.

REFERENCES

Arnold, J. H., 1944. Unsteady-state vaporization and absorption. *Trans. American Institute of Chemical Engineers*, Vol. 40, pp. 361–379.

Cohen, Y., W. Cocchio, and D. Mackay, 1978. Laboratory studies of liquid phase controlled volatilization rates in the presence of wind waves. *Environmental Science & Technology*. Vol. 12, p. 553–558.

Farmer, W. J., et al., 1980. Land Disposal of Hexachlorobenzene Wastes—Controlling Vapor Movement in Soil, U.S. EPA-600/2-80-119.

Freeman, R. A., 1979. Stripping of hazardous chemicals from surface aerated waste treatment basins. In: APCA/WPCF Specialty conference on control of specific toxic pollutants. Gainesville, Florida. Feb, 13–16, 1979.

Hwang, S. T., 1986. Mathematical Model Selection Criteria for Performing Exposures Assessments: Airborne Contaminants from Hazardous Waste Facilities. Draft Technical Support Document, U.S. EPA/ORD, Washington, D.C.

Liss, P. S., and P. G. Slater, 1974. Flux of Gases Across the Air–Sea Surface. *Nature*, No. 274, p. 181.

Mackay, D., and P. L. Leinonen, 1975. Rate of Evaporation of Low-Solubility Contaminants from Water Bodies to Atmosphere. *Environmental Science and Technology*, Vol. 9, p. 13.

McCord, A. T., 1981. Study of the Emission Rate of Volatile Compounds from Lagoons, *Proceedings* of the Second National Conference of Management of Uncontrolled Hazardous Waste Sites, Washington, D.C.

NYSDEC, 1991. New York State Air Guide—1, Guidelines for the Control of Toxic Ambient Air Contaminants, Department of Environmental Conservation, Division of Air.

Owen, M. R., R. W. Edwards, and J. W. Gibbs, 1964. Some Reaeration Studies in Streams, *International J. Air and Water Pollution*, Vol. 8, p. 496.

Shen, T. T., 1982a. Estimation of Organic Compound Emissions from Waste Lagoons, *J. APCA*, Vol. 32, No. 1, pp. 79–82 (Jan.).

Shen, T. T., 1982b. Air Quality Assessment for Land Disposal of Industrial Waste, *Environmental Management*, Vol. 5, p. 297.

Shen, T. T., 1984. Air Pollution Assessment: Toxic Emission from Hazardous Waste Lagoon and Landfills, *Proceedings* of the International Seminar on Environmental Impact Assessment, University of Aberdeen, Scotland, UK, July.

Shen, T. T., et al., 1985. Validation of Mathematical Models Predicting the Airborne Chemical Emission Rates from Saturated Soils, Preprint Paper No. 85-73.4 of the APCA Annual Meeting, Detroit, MI, June.

Shen, T. T., and T. J. Tofflemire. 1980. Air pollution aspects of land disposal of toxic wastes. Environmental Engineering Division Journal. *106*:211–226, 1980.

Smith, J. H., and D. C. Bomberger, 1980. Prediction of Volatilization Rates of High-Volatility Chemicals from Natural Water Bodies, *Environmental Science and Technology,* Vol. 14, No. 11.

Thibodeaux, L. J., 1981. Estimating the Air Emissions of Chemicals from Hazardous Waste Landfills, *Journal of Hazardous Materials,* Vol. 4, pp. 235–244.

U.S. EPA, 1978. Guidelines on Air Quality Models. EPA-450/4-79-030, OAQPS. Research Triangle Park, NC.

U.S. EPA, 1979. Industrial Source Complex (ISC) Dispersion Model User's Guide—I. EPA-450/2-78-027, OAQPS. Research Triangle Park, NC.

U.S. EPA, 1986. Guideline on Air Quality Models (Revised). EPA-450/2-78-027, OAQPS. Research Triangle Park, NC.

U.S. EPA, 1987. Hazardous Waste TSDF—Air Emission Models. EPA-450/3-87-026.

U.S. EPA, 1989. Hazardous Waste Treatment, Storage, and Disposal Facilities (TSDF) Air Emission Models. EPA-450/3-87-026, OAQPS, Research Triangle Park, NC.

U.S. EPA, 1990. Air/Superfund National Technical Guidance Study Series: Development of Example Procedures for Evaluating the Air Impacts of Soil Excavation Associated With Superfund Remedial Actions. OAQPS, Research Triangle Park, NC.

U.S. EPA, 1991. Hazardous Waste TSDF—Background information of proposed RCRA air emission standards, draft document. OAQPS/RTP, EPA-450/3-89-023a.

7

Health Risk Assessment and VOC Pathway Analysis

INTRODUCTION

As discussed in previous chapters, the volatile organic compound (VOC) pathway analysis is a systematic approach that involves the application of measurement and/or modeling to estimate emission rates and concentrations of VOCs (USEPA, 1989a). VOC pathway analysis comprises three primary components:

- Characterization of VOC emission sources (e.g., estimation of chemical emission rates)
- Determination of atmospheric processes (e.g., transport and dilution)
- Evaluation of receptor exposure potential (e.g., VOC exposure point concentrations)

The emphasis of VOC pathway analysis is to provide a consistent and technically adequate data base when conducting risk assessments for Remedial Investigations/Feasibility Studies (RI/FS). The following sections describe in detail what is a risk assessment and how the three components of VOC pathway analysis are included in the four steps of a risk assessment as proposed by the National Research Council (NRC, 1983).

HEALTH RISK ASSESSMENT

An environmental health risk assessment attempts to describe the potential risks to humans associated with exposure to environmental contaminants in a logical and meaningful way. This information is important because we are all constantly exposed to various levels of chemicals in the air we breathe and the food and water we eat and drink. Many of these

127

chemicals occur naturally, while others are products of our urban environment. We know that exposure to chemical contaminants can be harmful, that we can be exposed to varying levels of some contaminants without causing adverse health effects, and that we can live healthy, productive lives while still being constantly exposed to contaminants resulting in a moderate degree of risk. The classical toxicology principle stated by Paracelsus over 400 years ago still holds true today: "All substances are poisons; there is none which is not a poison. The right dose differentiates a poison and a remedy" (Doull and Bruce, 1986).

As a result, our interest in controlling the amount of contaminants to which we are exposed is not to reduce the risk to zero, but to try to control the risks by reducing our exposures to levels that will not cause adverse health effects. Providing the basis for defining those levels of exposure constitutes a VOC pathway risk assessment.

COMPONENTS OF A RISK ASSESSMENT

Risk assessment is a process where qualitative and quantitative determinations of health risks posed by environmental contamination are evaluated. Risk assessments are increasingly relied upon by federal, state, and local authorities as a tool for decision-making and policy development on environmental issues. A health risk assessment consists of four steps (Figure 7-1), as originally defined by the National Research Council (NRC, 1983) and subsequently adapted by U.S. EPA (1989d) and other regulatory agencies:

- Data Collection and Evaluation: Gather and analyze relevant data and identify potential chemicals of concern (also referred to as Hazard Identification).
- Toxicity Assessment: Collect qualitative and quantitative toxicity information and identify appropriate toxicity criteria.
- Exposure Assessment: Identify populations exposed to the contaminants of concern and determine the types, magnitudes, frequencies, and durations of exposure to these contaminants by various routes of exposure (Air Pathway Analysis).
- Risk Characterization: Characterize and describe potential adverse health effects and the magnitude of risks to human health, compare exposures with federal, state, and local criteria, and evaluate uncertainty in the risk estimates.

A detailed description of these four components is provided in Risk Assessment Guidance For Superfund (RAGS), Human Health Evaluation Manual (USEPA, 1989d). U.S. EPA has also issued Supplemental Guid-

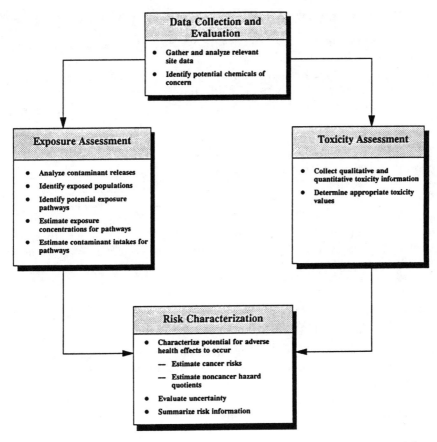

FIGURE 7-1.   Four components of a human health risk assessment.   (*Source:* U.S. EPA, 1989d).

ance for the Human Health Evaluation Manual: "Standard Default Exposure Factors" (USEPA, 1991a).

Other guidance documents applicable to assessing air pathway risks include Methodology for the Assessment of Health Risks Associated with Multiple Pathway Exposure to Municipal Waste Combustor Emissions (USEPA, 1986a), Methodology for Assessing Health Risks Associated with Indirect Exposure to Combustor Emissions (USEPA, 1990b), and Multi-Pathway Health Risk Assessment Input Parameters Guidance Document (Clement, 1988).

Application of the four steps of risk assessment in an Air Pathway Analysis is discussed in more detail in the following sections.

DATA COLLECTION AND EVALUATION

The first step in the risk assessment process characterizes VOC emission sources. It includes the gathering and analyzing of point and area source data relevant to characterizing human exposures and identifies substances that may present a risk to human health. In this assessment, collection of data includes the modeling or measurement/monitoring of VOC emissions.

The usefulness and validity of the health risk assessment is primarily limited by the accuracy and quality of VOC emissions data and/or concentration data, and the toxicological and environmental data used in estimating risk. If available data are insufficient, assumptions are made on the basis of the best scientific information and judgment available. These assumptions are carefully documented so that their validity and effects on the results may be judged. Assumptions are generally conservative to ensure that public health and the environment are protected to the greatest degree possible.

CHARACTERIZATION OF VOC
EMISSION MECHANISMS

VOC emissions can be classified as either point or area source emissions and VOCs can be present in all environmental media (Table 7-1). Point sources would include vents (e.g., landfill methane gas vents) and stacks (e.g., incinerator and air strippers), whereas area sources are associated with fugitive emissions (e.g., landfills, lagoons or evaporation impoundments).

VOC emissions from point and area sources can be released through a variety of mechanisms:

- Volatilization
- Biodegradation
- Photodecomposition
- Hydrolysis
- Combustion

The importance of each release mechanism is determined by the source (Table 7-2).

Volatilization is the most important mechanism for VOC releases and occurs when molecules of a dissolved or pure substance escapes to an adjacent gas layer (USEPA, 1989a). For wastes present at the surface, such escape results in immediate transport of the VOC into the atmosphere. Volatilization from subsurface wastes (e.g., leaking underground

TABLE 7-1. Most frequently reported substances at 546 national priority list sites.

Substance Identified at Hazardous Waste Disposal Sites	Sites[a]	Air Number of Sites (Rank)[b,c]	Ground Water Number of Sites (Rank)[b]	Surface Water Number of Sites (Rank)[b]
Most Frequently Occurring				
1. Trichloroethylene	179	8 (5)	127 (1)	49 (3)
2. Lead	162	7 (6)	77 (4)	84 (1)
3. Toluene	153	1 (3)	81 (3)	40 (4)
4. Benzene	143	1 (2)	84 (2)	36 (5)
5. Polychlorinated Biphenyls (PCBs)	121	6 (4)	29 (21)	54 (2)
6. Chloroform	111	1	70 (6)	24 (11)
7. Tetrachloroethylene	90	3 (16)	57 (7)	17 (14)
8. Phenol	84	3 (16)	43 (9)	28 (8)
9. Arsenic	84	2 (17)	45 (8)	35 (6)
10. Cadmium	82	31 (17)	28 (16)	28 (9)
11. Chromium	80	1	34 (14)	33 (7)
12. 1,1,1-Trichloroethane	79	3 (18)	58 (6)	20 (12)
13. Zinc and Compounds	74	2	28 (17)	27 (10)
14. Ethyl Benzene	73	7 (7)	36 (12)	14 (20)
15. Xylene	71	9 (4)	32 (15)	8 (25)
16. Methylene Chloride	63	2	36 (13)	17 (15)
17. Trans-1,2-Dichloroethylene	59	1	42 (10)	17 (16)
18. Mercury	54	4 (10)	27 (20)	20 (13)
19. Copper and Compounds	47	6	17 (24)	16 (18)
20. Cyanides (Soluble Salts)	46	2	16 (25)	16 (19)
21. Vinyl Chloride	44	4 (11)	28 (18)	10 (23)
22. 1,2-Dichloroethane	44	2	25 (21)	17 (17)
23. Chlorobenzene	42	0	23 (23)	9 (23)
24. 1,1-Dichloroethane	42	0	28 (19)	8 (24)
25. Carbon Tetrachloride	40	2	25 (22)	12 (21)

[a] Number of sites at which substance is present. Substances may be present in one, two, or all three environmental media at all sites at which it is known to be present. Therefore, the number of sites at which each substance is detected in environmental media may not equal the number in this column.

[b] Not all ranks will be represented in all media because not all chemicals found in media are among those found most frequently at site.

[c] Volatile organics not otherwise specified were reported as being detected most often (rank 1) in the air medium.

Source: USEPA, 1990a.

TABLE 7-2. Air emission mechanisms—gas phase emissions.

	Volatilization	Biodegradation	Photo-decomposition	Hydrolysis	Combustion
Pre-Remediation Sources					
• Landfills	I	S	N	N	S
• Lagoons	I	I	S	S	N
• Contaminated Soil Surfaces	I	I	N	N	N
• Open Containers (above-ground)	I	I	S	S	S
Remediation Sources					
• Soil Handling	I	N	N	N	N
• Air Stripper	I	N	N	N	N
• Incinerator	S	N	N	N	I
• Soil Vapor Extraction	I	N	N	N	N
• Solidification/Stabilization	I	N	N	N	N
Post-Remediation Sources					
• Landfills	I	S	N	N	N
• Lagoons	I	I	S	S	N
• Soil Surfaces	I	I	N	N	N
• Open Containers (above-ground)	I	I	S	S	N

Key: I = Important
S = Secondary
N = Negligible or Not Applicable

Source: USEPA, 1989a.

storage tanks) results in a concentration gradient in the soil-gas from the waste to the surface (USEPA, 1989a). The rate of emissions of VOCs from subsurfaces is primarily limited by the rate of diffusion of contaminants to the soil-air interface. The rate of volatilization of VOCs at the soil-air boundary is a function of concentration and properties of the escaping chemical, soil properties (moisture, temperature, clay content, and organic matter content), and properties of the air at soil level (temperature, relative humidity, and wind speed) (USEPA, 1989a).

The rate of volatilization from liquid surfaces is dependent on the concentration of the contaminants in the boundary layer of liquid at the liquid-air interface. Any factor that enhances mixing in the bulk liquid and replenishment of contaminants in the boundary layer will enhance the volatilization rate. It is important to note that compounds referred to as volatile and semi-volatile are broad categories of chemicals (Table 7-3) and further subdivision by vapor pressure, toxicity, etc., may be necessary to properly evaluate air emissions (USEPA, 1989a).

Other processes, such as biodegradation, photodecomposition, hydrolysis, and combustion, can act to increase the rate of emissions of VOCs from any type of waste (USEPA, 1989a). Biodegradation takes place when microbes break down organic compounds via metabolic processes. Biodegradation can be an important mechanism for gas-phase emissions from wastes in the upper layers of soils or ponds. The rate of organic compound decomposition depends on the structure of the compound, the

TABLE 7-3.   Examples of broad-band, class, and indicator species.

Broad Band	Classes of Compounds	Indicator Species
Volatile Organics	Aliphatics	Alkanes, Total Hydrocarbons as Pentane
	Aromatics	Benzene, Xylene, Toluene
	Halogenated Species	Trichloroethene, Trichloroethane, Vinyl Chloride
	Oxygenated Species	Ethanol, Formaldehyde
	Sulfur Containing Species	Mercaptans, Thiophenes
	Nitrogen Containing Species	Benzonitrile
Volatile Inorganics	Acid Gases	Sulfur Dioxide, Hydrogen Chloride
	Sulfur Containing	Hydrogen Sulfide
Semi-Volatile Organics	Polynuclear Aromatics (PAH)	Napathalene, Benzo-(a)Pyrene
	Polychlorinated Biphenols (PCBs)	PCBs as Aroclor 1254
Non-Volatiles	Metals	Lead, Chromium, Zinc

Source: USEPA, 1990a.

metabolic requirements of the microbes, and the amount of moisture, oxygen, and nutrients available to the microbes. Photodecomposition can occur when a hazardous chemical absorbs light or when energy is transferred because of light absorption by surrounding elements. Hydrolysis occurs when a chemical reacts with water. For organic compounds, the reaction usually replaces a functional group with a hydroxyl. Combustion, the process of burning, can be a source of organic and inorganic emissions. Inorganic emissions are encountered when temperatures inside the combustion chamber are greater than the compounds' respective boiling points (e.g., mercury). Emissions from combustion sources may also include absorbed or adsorbed volatile and semi-volatile organic compounds following recondensation onto particulates.

VOC AIR PATHWAY ANALYSIS

Emission rate data can be obtained from a variety of approaches including direct and indirect measurement, line monitoring and modeling, or predictive modeling (USEPA, 1989a). Dispersion modeling is the primary approach to characterizing atmospheric processes and predicting ambient concentrations. Air emission models are used to estimate chemical-specific emission rates based on source input data. These models have been validated against pilot-scale and field test results. Nevertheless, the models attempt to predict complex physical and chemical phenomena and should be used carefully because of the inherent uncertainty associated with theoretical assumptions (USEPA, 1989a).

Emission rate measurement or air monitoring is an alternative approach to determining emission rates and air concentrations at specific receptor locations where accurate, site-specific data are needed (e.g., school yards, hospitals). Detailed procedures for the selection of appropriate modeling or measurement/monitoring approaches for source-specific VOC pathway analysis can be found in Air/Superfund National Technical Guidance Study Series, Vols. I–IV (USEPA, 1989a,b,c; 1990a). These guidance documents are designed especially for conducting air pathway analyses (APA) for Superfund activities. The APA documents are designed to serve the needs of the remedial program manager (RPM) and others for designing and conducting APA and using APA data for the remediation of National Priority List (NPL) sites.

SELECTION OF CHEMICALS
OF CONCERN

The risks to public health vary with different contaminants. Some highly toxic chemicals may be present in very small amounts, whereas other chemicals with lower toxicity may be present in relatively large quantities. The selection of contaminants of concern is a critical early step in risk assessment. The degree of risk for a given chemical will depend on its inherent toxicity, the quantities in which it is emitted, its behavior in the environment, and the degree to which it is absorbed after inhalation, ingestion, or dermal contact. As a means of reducing the number of chemicals to evaluate in the risk assessment to a manageable number, these properties are taken into account in a preliminary screen of the relative contribution each chemical may make to the overall risk. Those chemicals accounting for most of the possible risk (usually >95% of the risk) are further evaluated in the risk assessment (USEPA, 1989d).

TOXICITY ASSESSMENT

Following the identification of potential chemicals of concern in the first step, the toxicity assessment defines the relationship between the dose of a chemical and the resulting health effects. This assessment results in a quantitative measure of a concentration or dose of a chemical above which humans are at risk for toxicity, or an estimate of carcinogenic potency or risk. It also includes qualitative aspects of the range of target organs, toxic effects, and sensitive populations that may be affected by chemicals of concern.

DOSE-RESPONSE RELATIONSHIPS

Key dose-response variables developed by the U.S. EPA for use in quantitative risk assessment are carcinogenic slope factors for evaluating cancer risks and reference doses (RfD) for evaluating risks of noncarcinogenic effects.

Carcinogenic Slope Factor

The carcinogenic slope factor (expressed in units of $mg/kg/day)^{-1}$ for ingestion, inhalation, and dermal pathways) is typically determined by the upper 95 percent confidence limit of the slope of the linearized multistage model, which expresses excess cancer risk as a function of dose. The model is based on high-to-low dose extrapolation, usually from animal studies but sometimes human epidemiology data, and also assumes that there is no threshold for the initiation of toxic effects.

Reference Dose and Reference Concentration

The chronic oral reference dose (RfD; expressed in units of mg/kg day) is an estimated daily chemical intake rate to a human population, including sensitive groups, that is not expected to result in adverse health effects. RfDs assume that threshold levels exist for the initiation of toxic effects. The threshold of observed effects (the No Observed Adverse Effect Level, or NOEAL) is divided by uncertainty factors to derive an RfD that is protective of the most sensitive members of the population.

The uncertainty factors used in calculating the RfDs reflect scientific judgment regarding the various types of data used to estimate the RfD. An uncertainty factor of 10 is usually used to account for variations in human sensitivity when extrapolating from valid human studies involving sub-chronic or long-term exposure of average, healthy subjects. An additional 10-fold factor is usually used for each of the following extrapolations: from long-term animal studies to the case of humans, from a Lowest Observed Adverse Effect Level (LOAEL) to a NOAEL, and from sub-chronic to chronic exposure. To reflect professional assessment of the uncertainties of the study and data base not explicitly addressed by the above uncertainty factors, an additional uncertainty factor or modifying factor, ranging from greater than 0 to less than or equal to 10 is applied (USEPA, 1992). Reference concentrations (RfC) are concentrations in air not expected to result in adverse effects if inhaled over a lifetime. They are derived in a similar fashion as RfDs using the inhalation pathway, or are extrapolated from the RfD.

Source of Toxicity Criteria

Carcinogenic slope factors and verified RfDs for chemicals of concern can be collated from a number of sources. Priority in reference sources is given to the U.S. EPA Integrated Risk Evaluation System (IRES) data-base, which publishes only current and verified carcinogenic slope factors, RfDs, and RfCs. Other sources that can be used include U.S. EPA Health Effects Assessment Summary Tables (HEAST) and U.S. EPA health advisory documents.

INTERACTION AMONG CHEMICALS

In addition to the need to completely characterize chemicals emitted from waste treatment and disposal facilities to which people are exposed, it is also necessary to identify potential interactions between chemicals in these mixtures. When exposure occurs to two chemicals simultaneously, there is maybe an increase or decrease in toxicity (Klaassen and Eaton, 1991). Frequently the toxicity of the combination is additive; i.e., the resulting toxicity is the sum of the effects of each chemical alone (2 + 2 =

4). Chemicals may also interact antagonistically, in which case the toxicity of one is reduced by the other $(2 + 2 = 3)$. Finally, and of most concern, synergistic interactions may occur. These result in increased overall toxicity $(2 + 2 = 10)$. Because there is no accepted methodology for calculating interactions among chemicals, the standard U.S. EPA methodology assumes that the effects of chemical mixtures are additive (USEPA, 1986b).

EXPOSURE ASSESSMENT

VOCs can be released directly to the atmosphere or may be present in soil and water and subsequently released to the atmosphere. VOCs released to the atmosphere can be redeposited on soil, water, and vegetation through wet/dry deposition and transferred into the terrestrial and aquatic food chain (Figure 7-2). Humans can be exposed to VOCs in various media by direct inhalation or indirectly through dermal contact, ingestion of soil and water, and/or ingestion of foods (plant or animal) grown in contaminated soil or water. The goal of VOC pathway analysis in the exposure assessment is to identify and estimate the type and magnitude of exposures to VOCs into the area of concern. The results of the exposure assessment are combined with chemical-specific toxicity information, developed in the Toxicity Assessment section, to characterize potential risks.

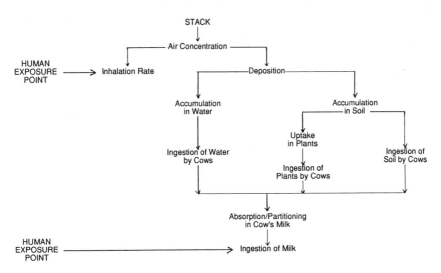

FIGURE 7-2.   Illustration of exposure pathways.   (*Source:* U.S. EPA, 1989d).

DETERMINATION OF
ATMOSPHERIC PROCESSES

The atmosphere is a major exposure pathway for the migration of VOC releases. Unlike other environmental media, the air pathway is characterized by short migration times, relatively large exposure areas, and difficulty in mitigating the potential consequences of a release after the contaminant enters the atmosphere. The fundamental atmospheric processes affecting airborne contaminants include atmospheric transport and diffusion, as well as transformation, deposition, and depletion. The extent to which these atmospheric processes act on the contaminant determines the magnitude, composition, and duration of the release, the route of human exposure, and the impact of the release on the environment.

Transport and Diffusion

VOCs may volatilize directly to the atmosphere from waste treatment and disposal facilities (e.g., landfills and lagoons) or migrate laterally into the surrounding soils and groundwater (USEPA, 1900a). Thus, large areas of contaminated subsurface soils and groundwater represent potential sources of VOC air emissions. Once released to the ambient air, a contaminant is subject to simultaneous transport and diffusion processes in the atmosphere. Atmospheric transport and diffusion conditions are significantly affected by meteorological, topographic, and source factors.

The contaminant will be carried by the ambient air following the spatial and temporal characteristics of the wind flow field determined by wind direction and speed conditions. The turbulent motions of the atmosphere, characterized by atmospheric stability conditions, promote diffusion or airborne gases and particulate matter. Local meteorology during and after the release determines where the contaminant moves and how it is diluted in the atmosphere. Terrain features, such as valleys, hills, and mountains, can also alter the transport and diffusion of a contaminant between its source and receptors. Source factors, such as the release height and the source configuration can also influence the transport and diffusion of VOC releases.

Transformation, Deposition, and Depletion

VOCs emitted to the atmosphere are subjected to a variety of physical and chemical influences. Transformation processes can lead to the formation of more hazardous substances, or, on the other hand, may result in hazardous constituents being converted into less harmful ones. VOCs may remain in the atmosphere for a considerable time and undergo changes through oxidation and photochemical reactions (Randerson, 1984). These effects are less important than transport and diffusion in determining contaminant fate, and are subject to more uncertainty. Contaminated soils can transfer VOCs into the air-filled spaces in the soil matrix. Contaminated soil gas can then be released to the atmosphere at the surface soil/atmosphere interface (USEPA, 1900a). VOC contaminated groundwater can also generate additional VOC emissions due to volatilization of dissolved contaminants in groundwater that are transferred into the soil gas and subsequently to the atmosphere (USEPA, 1900a).

Airborne VOCs can become depleted from the atmosphere by the natural cleansing process of wet deposition. Wet deposition involves the incorporation of toxic pollutants into various forms of precipitation (e.g., rain, fog, snow), with subsequent deposition onto soil, water, and vegetation.

Although deposition depletes concentrations of VOCs in air, it increases the concentration of contaminants in soils, water, and vegetation. Chemical transport in soil and surface water and steady-state concentrations are the result of wet deposition onto soil and surface water and loss due to leaching, abiotic and biotic degradation, and revolatilization. Chemical migration to groundwater may also result from surface recharge of the aquifers and/or lateral migration of VOCs through the soil profile from subsurface impoundments. The presence of VOCs in soils is dependent on the soil organic carbon sorption coefficients (Koc), which indicates the mobility of VOCs in soils (ATSDSR, 1991). Soil conditions such as pH, soil structure and characteristics, organic matter content, and water content affect the distribution and mobility of chemicals after deposition onto soil. In addition, chemicals deposited on soil surfaces may be incorporated into the lower soil profiles by tilling, whether done manually in a garden or mechanically in a large field.

EVALUATION OF RECEPTOR
EXPOSURE POTENTIAL

An evaluation of receptor exposure potential is conducted in the risk assessment to identify potential exposure pathways of concern and exposed populations. Estimates of exposure concentrations and contaminant intakes rates for exposed populations are determined based on modeling and/or monitoring data.

Potential Exposure Pathways

Exposure pathways are the means by which chemicals are transported through the environment (air, water, soil, biota) and reach offsite receptors, where they are inhaled, ingested, or absorbed through the skin (Figure 7-2). An exposure pathway consists of exposed environmental media and the routes by which individuals contact these contaminated media. Humans can be exposed to VOC release by direct inhalation (USEPA, 1986a), but also indirectly by such exposures as consumption of and dermal contact with chemicals in soil and water, consumption of fruit and vegetables grown in contaminated soils and/or irrigated with contaminant water, consumption of animals that have ingested contaminated soil, water, or vegetation, and consumption of fish living in contaminated water (USEPA, 1990b). Potential pathways are discussed below by route of exposure.

Inhalation

The primary mode of exposure to VOCs released to the atmosphere is direct inhalation. Absorption in the lung is usually high because of the large surface area and close proximity and permeability of blood vessels to the exposed surface area. The dose to exposed individual depends on the ventilation rate, body weight, retention fraction, exposure concentration of VOCs, and chemical and physical characteristics of the VOCs.

Exposure to VOCs while showering is another potentially important route of exposure. Because of the presence of VOCs in groundwater due to lateral migration of VOCs from subsurface impoundments (e.g., landfills or lagoons), VOCs can be released while showering and reach concentration levels in the air several times greater than baseline concentrations (Wallace, 1990).

Other potential pathways of exposure to VOC due to wet deposition and/or contamination of soil and groundwater by chemicals leaching from subsurface impoundments would include the ingestion of contaminated crops, water, and soil by animals and/or humans, ingestion of contaminated animal products, and dermal contact with contaminants in soil and water (Crume and Caldwell, 1990).

Ingestion

Ingestion of soil is a primary route of exposure to chemicals in soil. Children are more likely than adults to ingest soil during outdoor play because of their more frequent hand-to-mouth behavior. Adults may also ingest small amounts of soil during gardening or while caring for pets.

Contaminated soils may also be transported to living quarters where inadvertent ingestion of house dust can contribute to contaminant intake.

Aerial wet deposition of contaminants on plant and soil surfaces, irrigation of crops with contaminated water, VOC contamination of soils, and soil turnover practices, uptake and assimilation by plants and animals, and subsequent consumption by human populations need to be considered as potential routes of exposure to VOCs. Contaminant deposition on leafy surfaces may be a source of exposure to contaminants of concern through leaf uptake of contaminants and/or ingestion of unwashed produce. Contaminants may potentially bioaccumulate in crops through root uptake of contaminants present in soil and/or adsorption of VOCs/SVOCs on plant life. Another likely source of exposure to VOCs is via ingestion of meat and/or dairy products from grazing animals. These animals may be exposed to contaminants in feedstocks, soil, water, and air.

VOCs may also contaminate surface water bodies through the process of wet deposition. Groundwater sources may become contaminated with VOCs due to lateral migration of VOCs through the soil profile. Humans may be exposed to VOCs through incidental ingestion of accumulated chemicals in surface water while swimming, showering, and from drinking contaminated groundwater or water from collected precipitation, such as a cistern or reservoirs.

In the aquatic environment, some partitioning of VOCs from the water column to sediment and suspended particulate organic matter may occur based on the Koc value and from water to tissues of exposed fish based on Kow value (ATSDR, 1991). Thus, factors that affect human exposure by ingestion of fish from a body of water include concentrations of contaminants in the sediment, water, and food eaten by fish (e.g., plants, macroinvertebrates), the type of fish consumed, the human consumption rates of the various fish groups, the bioconcentration factor for these groups, and the percent of the dietary fish that are caught in bodies of water near the source. For most chemicals and situations, contaminants in water are considered to be the main source of exposure for fish (Clement, 1988).

Dermal Contact

In addition to inhalation and ingestion, dermal absorption is one of the three main pathways of exposure to chemicals by humans. However, the dermal absorption pathway is associated with the greatest amount of scientific and regulatory uncertainty for assessing exposure (e.g., contact time, contact amount, surface area, and rate of absorption). The ability of a compound to penetrate the skin is dependent on two physical events: (1) the compound must first diffuse or desorb from media (soil or water) to the skin surface, and (2) the contaminant must penetrate the skin. Nevertheless, dermal absorption can potentially be a significant route of exposure for a number of chemicals and can contribute to systemic levels of these chemicals.

For organic chemicals, dermal absorption from soil depends on such properties as molecular weight and the propensity of a compound to absorb to organic matter in soil. Generally, smaller molecules are able to penetrate the skin more readily than larger molecules. The soil-matrix effect is reported to decrease absorption of organic chemicals in two ways: (1) by decreasing the amount of direct contact of the compound with the skin, and (2) by binding to soil particles. Binding to soil particles is directly related to the organic content of the soil and the lipophilic nature of the chemical (Clement, 1988; USEPA, 1990b).

Once VOCs that are depleted from the atmosphere by wet deposition reach water sources, humans may be exposed by absorption through the skin while swimming or bathing. Many of the factors that influence dermal absorption from soil also influence dermal absorption from water; thus the uncertainties associated with the soil pathway can be assumed to apply to the water pathway. Exposure due to dermal absorption from water is likely to be influenced by the contaminant concentration in water and the extent of contact.

Populations at Risk

Populations at greatest risk from exposure to VOCs are year-round, lifelong residents at the location of maximum ambient air concentrations and deposition. If year-round, life-long residents exposed to the maximum amount of emissions are not at risk by regulatory standards, then it follows that visitors to the area or those not exposed for an entire lifetime will also not be at risk because exposure would be correspondingly lower.

Subpopulations that may be more sensitive to chemical exposures include infants and children, elderly people, pregnant and nursing women, and people suffering from chronic illness. Several investigations have shown sensitivity in young children, whereas data on elderly people are less available. Uncertainty factors in exposure criteria are intended to take the increased susceptibilities of children, elderly, and chronically ill into account.

The fetus is potentially vulnerable since many functions are not fully developed until after birth, and several possibilities exist for contact between the fetus and external compounds via exposure of the mother. However, exposure to toxic levels of compounds is generally modulated by maternal absorption which is often less than a young child. Infants, on the other hand, have higher absorption rate, higher whole-body retention, and much higher accumulation in the brain compared to the adult exposed under similar conditions.

Although the fetus and infants may be more developmentally sensitive, young children are often considered more at risk because of their greater potential for exposure combined with physiological sensitivity. Children are more susceptible to toxic effects to organic and inorganic compounds for a number of reasons: (1) much more efficient absorption of many substances from the gastrointestinal tract than adults, (2) increased prevalence of dietary deficiencies of essential vitamins and nutrients, (3) higher metabolic rate relative to body mass, thereby affecting dose per body weight, and (4) lower thresholds for adverse effects of noncarcinogenic chemicals. The greater hand-to-mouth activity in children leads to increased ingestion of soils relative to adults, thereby enhancing their sensitivity to the health effects posed by chemicals in the environment.

Evaluation of Exposure

For the evaluation of VOC emissions data, U.S. EPA (1989d) recommends for the Superfund program, for instance, that exposures be calculated under a reasonable maximum exposure (RME) condition. The RME scenario incorporates a number of conservative assumptions in determining chemical intake rates and duration of exposure in order to estimate the reasonable maximum exposure for any exposure pathway. Average exposure may also be calculated and is based on estimates of more typical exposure conditions. Calculating risks by this procedure provides a range of estimates generally more useful for risk management decisions than are single risk estimates.

Exposure parameters for both RME and typical scenarios can be found in current U.S. EPA guidelines (USEPA, 1989d, 1991a,b). These guidelines give estimates under RME and average exposure scenarios for residential exposures and RME scenario for industrial exposures.

For each route of exposures, age-specific intake factors are calculated for chemicals of concern using pathway-specific equations. These factors are a combined representation of all exposure parameters that remain constant for all chemicals of concern (e.g., body weight, intake rates, unit correction factors). Calculations of exposure factors are made for each pathway and for each scenario (average and RME). Chemical-specific absorption factors may be included should differences occur between absorption by the receptor and by the study subjects for which toxicity criteria were derived.

Age-specific intake factors are calculated by the following equation:

Age-Specific Intake = (IR × CF × EF × ED × AB)/(BW × AT)

where:
  IR = intake rate (e.g., mg/day)
  EF = exposure frequency (days/year)
  ED = exposure duration (years)
  CF = correction factor
  AB = appropriate fractional absorption correction
  BW = body weight (kg)
  AT = averaging time (days)

The exposure assessment will estimate chemical specific intakes for the receptors and exposure pathways. Intake rates are expressed as milligram per kilogram of body weight per day (mg/kg/day). Calculation of chemical intakes are based on site-specific information, on consumption rates, and on U.S. EPA recommended estimates of exposure rates.

For each route of exposure and age group, a dose is calculated for chemicals of concern by the equation:

$$Dose = EC \times Age\text{-}Specific\ Intake$$

where:
  EC = exposure concentration (e.g., $\mu g/m^3$)

The dose calculated for each route of exposure and age group is defined as the average lifetime daily dose for a receptor following exposure to VOCs. These values are then used to calculate carcinogenic and noncarcinogenic risks under the final step in the risk assessment process.

RISK CHARACTERIZATION

The final step in the risk assessment process summarizes and combines information from the toxicity and exposure assessments to characterize carcinogenic and noncarcinogenic risks from exposure to VOCs in the environment.

NONCARCINOGENIC RISK

As discussed under the Toxicity Assessment, U.S. EPA regulatory guidelines differentiate between the effects of known or suspected carcinogenic compounds and the noncarcinogenic effects of a number of substances. For noncarcinogenic effects, a threshold of exposure forms the basis for the RfD for chronic exposure, below which adverse effects are not expected to occur. To estimate noncarcinogenic risks, a hazard quotient, the dose-to-RfD ratio, is calculated by dividing the estimated dose by the RfD:

$$\text{Hazard Quotient} = \text{Average Daily Dose (mg/kg/day)}/\text{RfD}$$

Hazard quotients exceeding unity (one) indicate a concern may exist for adverse noncarcinogenic health effects to the exposed population. Hazard quotients of one or below are thus considered by U.S. EPA to be protective of public health. Hazard quotients resulting in adverse effects by similar mechanisms should be added.

CARCINOGENIC RISK

For carcinogenic compounds, the risk is calculated by comparing the average lifetime dose to the route-specific carcinogenic slope factor of the compound being evaluated:

$$\text{Risk} = \text{Average Lifetime Dose (mg/kg/day)} * \text{Slope Factor (mg/kg/day)}^{-1}$$

The risk estimates are unitless and refer to the calculated probability of contracting cancer at that exposure. Cancer estimates assume additive effects in accordance with U.S. EPA guidance, and no synergistic or antagonistic effects among the carcinogenic compounds as we currently have no reliable means of accurately quantifying these factors. Thus, once risks are calculated for each chemical of concern, a total risk for the pathway is calculated by summing the risks for each compound. An overall risk is then determined by summing the risks from each pathway. A one-in-a-million risk has been used by U.S. EPA and many state agencies as a starting level for regulatory decisions, although it is not a regulatory standard (Kelly and Cardon, 1991). Due to the causervativeness inherent in both the toxicity and exposure assessments, calculated risks are considered to the upper-bound risks. Actual risks will likely be lower than the calculated risks and may be substantially lower, approaching zero.

UNCERTAINTY ANALYSIS

In most health risk assessments, especially those regarding chronic hazards, many assumptions in estimates of exposure and chemical toxicity must be made due to the lack of data. The assumptions that are made during the risk assessment should be based on sound scientific information and facility-specific conditions, and the rationale for their use should be explicitly stated. It is standard practice to include a comprehensive explanation of all the assumptions that are made during a risk assessment and their contribution to the uncertainty in the assessment. In this way, others reviewing the data can quickly determine the quality and degree of conservatism of the assumptions used in the health risk assessment.

Risk estimates from the different pathways are associated with varying degrees of uncertainty. Because uncertainty is multiplied with every assumption, risks due to pathways involving many assumptions are inherently more highly overestimated than pathways of more direct exposure. In addition, assumptions used to bridge data gaps in risk assessment are intentionally conservative so that risk will not be underestimated. The result of multiple upper-bound assumptions is that pathways with many transfer steps, such as drinking milk from cows that grazed on exposed soil, can result in greatly overestimated risk as compared to simple pathways such as breathing emission in the air. Use of site-specific data wherever possible allows a more accurate risk assessment to be made.

To illustrate the relative amounts of conservative assumptions that might be incorporated by such pathways, Figure 7-3 exhibits the chemical transfer steps via inhalation and drinking cow's milk (Blanchet and Kelly,

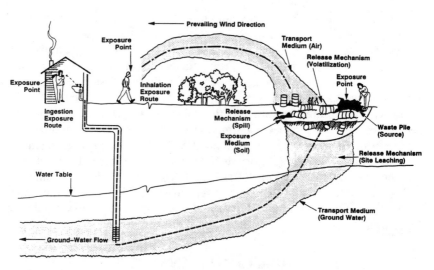

FIGURE 7-3.   Levels of added uncertainty for exposure via inhalation versus ingestion of cow's milk.   (*Source:* Blanchet and Kelly, in preparation).

in preparation). The numerous assumptions and uncertainty factors required to assess exposure via milk, multiplied at each step, might account for initial predictions of greater risk by this pathway relative to inhalation. However, closer examination of information using more accurate data in place of overly conservative assumptions shows that inhalation generally remains the major source of risk.

SUMMARY

The demands of risk assessment of VOCs require that risk assessors consider a number of parameters when evaluating VOC emissions from waste treatment and disposal facilities. Risk assessors must adequately characterize the sources of VOC emissions from a facility, selection of chemicals of concern and resulting toxicity, potential direct and indirect exposure pathways, populations at risk, and potential carcinogenic and noncarcinogenic health effects.

Although there is no specific risk assessment guidance for evaluating risks posed by VOC releases from waste treatment and disposal facilities, U.S. EPA has issued risk assessment guidance for the evaluation of exposure to combustion air emissions and to releases from hazardous waste sites. This guidance is currently the most peer-reviewed and widely used methodology by risk assessors. In addition, a number of recently developed exposure parameters, published by U.S. EPA, have improved the accuracy of evaluating potential adverse health effects from exposure to many types of hazardous emissions.

REFERENCES

Agency for Toxic Substances and Disease Registry (ATSDR). 1991. Toxicological Profile for Trichloroethylene. Draft. Oak Ridge, TN.

Blanchet, R. and K. Kelly. In preparation. Fundamentals of risk assessment for hazardous waste incinerators. Environmental Toxicology International, Seattle, WA.

Clement Associates, Inc. 1988. Multi-Pathway Health Risk Assessment Input Parameters Guidance Document. Prepared for State of California, Department of Health Services. Berkeley: California Department of Health Services.

Crume, R. V. and M.-J. Caldwell. 1990. Concerns regarding the application of air toxics risk assessments to regulatory decision-making. 83rd Annual Meeting and Exhibition of Air and Waste Management Association, Pittsburgh, PA.

Doull, J. and M. C. Bruce. 1986. Origin and scope of toxicology. In Casarett and Doull's Toxicology: The Basic Science of Poisons. 4th ed. Eds. M. O. Amdur, J. Doull, and C. Klaassen. Chapter 1, 3–11. New York: Pergamon.

Kelly, K. and N. Cardon. 1991. The myth of 10^{-6} as a definition of acceptable risk. Presented at the 84th Annual Meeting of the Air and Waste Management Association. Vancouver, B.C. June 1991.

Klaassen, C. and D. Eaton. 1991. Principles of toxicology. In Casarett and Doull's Toxicology: The Basic Science of Poisons. 4th ed. Eds. M. O. Amdur, J. Doull, and C. Klaassen. Chapter 2, 12–49. New York: Pergamon.

National Research Council (NRC). 1983. Risk Assessment in the Federal Government: Managing the Process. National Research Council, National Academy of Sciences. Washington, D.C.: National Academy Press.

Randerson, D. (Ed.). 1984. Atmospheric Science and Power Production. DOE/TIC-27601, U.S. Department of Energy, Washington, D.C.

U.S. Environmental Protection Agency (USEPA). 1986a. Methodology for assessment of health risks associated with multiple pathway exposure to municipal waste combustor emissions. Research Triangle Park, North Carolina: Office of Air Quality Planning and Standards.

U.S. Environmental Protection Agency (USEPA). 1986b. Superfund public health evaluation manual. EPA 540/1-86-060.

U.S. Environmental Protection Agency (USEPA). 1989a. Air/Superfund National Technical Guidance Study Series, Vol. I: Application of Air Pathway Analyses for Superfund Activities.

8

Control Technologies and Costs

The control of emission sources falls into four categories: hazardous waste treatment, storage, and disposal facilities (TSDFs); remediation of uncontrolled hazardous waste sites; industrial waste treatment; and municipal waste treatment. The characteristics of the emission sources are discussed first, along with the normally accepted control technology alternatives. Detailed discussions of the control technology alternatives follow, with the control technologies arranged in logical groups.

OVERVIEW OF EMISSION SOURCES AND AVAILABLE CONTROL STRATEGIES

Hazardous Waste Treatment, Storage, and Disposal Facilities (TSDFs)

TSDFs typically utilize liquids-treatment processes, such as neutralization, oxidation, precipitation, and physical separation, and thermal processes, such as incineration (*Federal Register*, 1991). The VOCs from liquids processes are controlled primarily by source control, process modifications, and/or covering. Off-gases from containment systems usually are adsorbed on activated carbon and/or thermally oxidized. Thermal waste treatment processes (incineration) are controlled primarily by operational parameters (combustion temperature profiles) or flue gas treatment (afterburners).

Remediation of Uncontrolled Hazardous Waste Sites

Uncontrolled sites are remediated by either in situ technologies (bioremediation, groundwater/vapor extraction) or gross removal. In situ

149

technologies inherently release smaller amounts of VOCs than does gross removal. There are many alternative control strategies for open waste sites, including foam, water, fill, wind screens, and polymer membranes. Because these technologies are unique to this application, they are discussed in a separate section at the end of this chapter.

Industrial Waste Treatment

Industrial waste treatment includes liquids-treatment processes for treating industrial wastewater and solids-treatment processes. The liquids and solids processes are very similar to those used for TSDFs. Control strategies utilized for these processes include source control, treatment process selection/modification, and containment. Exhaust air from containment facilities usually is adsorbed on activated carbon and/or thermally oxidized.

Municipal Waste Treatment

Municipal waste treatment facilities also called publicly owned treatment works (POTWs), include liquids processes for treating wastewater (sewage) and solids processes for treating wastewater residuals and municipal solid waste. These emission sources are usually much more dilute, but encompass much larger areas and air volumes, than the above sources. There now is very little operational VOC control equipment installed at POTWs. The most promising control strategy for POTWs is source control integrated into the existing NPDES Industrial Pretreatment Program. Other control strategies include process selection/modification and containment. Most containment structures for POTWs are so large that control of the ventilation air is not practical. However, some processes that have small containment areas, heat drying, for example, use thermal oxidation for emission control. Many POTWs have extensive odor control systems, but it is not known at this time how effective these systems are at controlling VOCs.

SOURCE CONTROL

Much has been published about the benefits of waste reduction at the source, because if smaller amounts of VOCs are generated in the waste, smaller amounts of VOCs must be collected, treated, stored, and destroyed. Also VOC emissions can be significantly reduced if organic compounds in the wastes can be recovered and reused, such as the solvents used in various industrial processes. This type of source control has been practiced for years at most POTWs as part of the NPDES Industrial Pretreatment Program.

Significant opportunities exist for industry to make cost-effective adjustments in processes that reduce VOCs at the source through:

- Improvements in housekeeping practices.
- On-site recycling and reuse.
- Equipment or technology modification.
- Process or procedure modification.
- Substitution of raw materials.
- Improvements in education and training.

The generation of organic-contaminated wastes can be reduced effectively by adopting certain in-plant practices. A typical example is minimizing the waste of solvents. Solvents are essential to industry and business, both large and small; they perform important roles in surface coatings, in dry cleaning, as carriers for other materials in chemical manufacturing processes, and in diluting or thinning paints and other products. The types of solvents usually found in wastewater are:

- Chlorinated solvents: methylene chloride, trichloroethylene, 1,1,1-trichloroethane, tetrachloroethylene, chloroform, and carbon tetrachloride.
- Oxygenated solvents: acetone, methyl ethyl ketone, butyl-cellosolve, and various alcohols, ethers, and amines.
- Aromatic hydrocarbon solvents: benzene, toluene, ethyl benzene, and xylene.
- Fluorocarbons: freon and chlorofluorocarbons.

Waste solvents can be successfully recovered from almost any industrial process where they are neither destroyed nor incorporated into the final product, but the recovery of waste solvents during industrial processes normally requires an economic justification. In the past the economic analysis of pollution costs has not included the liability costs of socioeconomic and ecological damage. However, recent events that have increased waste treatment and disposal costs, regulatory requirements, and the concern about legal liability also have altered waste generators' attitudes about the effort that should be expended to minimize waste generation.

In many instances, organic liquids used as solvents, lubricants, and cleaning agents can be replaced with aqueous (water-based) solutions. Aqueous alternatives have been developed for metal-working fluids that serve the dual function of lubrication and heat removal during machine cutting, and also are available for degreasing operations to replace organic process fluids. Such material substitutions often are motivated by environmental and economic consequences of the use of the product as well as of the management of the waste.

Preventive measures are ideal ways to reduce VOC emissions in waste through physical and procedural means before they are handled or treated at the POTW and the TSDF. Sludges and organic wastes that readily generate gases and leachate are known to contribute a significant amount of VOCs; so liquids containing organic compounds in waste landfills should be controlled because of their potential for contamination of not only ambient air but also ground waste. Preventing rainwater from both entering and leaving landfills eventually would minimize gas emissions.

Waste devolatilization will include the use of technology such as the thin film evaporator, with the actual type of devolatilization equipment depending on the characteristics of the waste to be treated. In such processes the waste is heated and/or stripped to reduce the volatile content. The VOCs are recovered through condensation in cooling equipment or possibly by using activated carbon.

Fugitive leaks can be a large component of the overall facility emissions. These emissions can be prevented through proper design and installation of leak-free equipment. The use of leak-tight valving and welding connections will add somewhat to the capital cost of the facility, but will not generally impact the operating costs.

The institution of a fugitive monitoring program with the use of leak-free equipment will dramatically reduce VOC emissions from fugitive sources. If pipe diameters exceed 1½ inches, joints can be welded instead of threaded. Also, technology currently exists for leak-free valves and leakless pump seals (such as magnetic pumps). This equipment can be used in new applications as a retrofit design. In many cases, the cost of leakless systems can be significant compared with conventional technology.

Wastes within the facility also can be segregated to allow effective reductions in VOCs. Highly volatile or highly toxic materials can be stored, handled, and treated in a manner that reduces VOC emissions. Low-volatility and low-hazard material may not require the same types of controls as more volatile and more toxic material, and, therefore, can be handled more cost-effectively than such material.

Segregation of wastes on-site is another preventive measure, designed to separate volatile from nonvolatile wastes. When segregation is used, the control of the volatiles can be done more cost-effectively than with nonsegregated material because the equipment will be used only on sources requiring control. The costs of segregating wastes usually includes added tankage for handling waste solvents, or possibly special handling area for highly volatile solid materials. The operation of a segregated waste system will increase operating costs only slightly.

Regulatory requirements such as the use of the manifest system and the waste management permit system provide steps and procedures designed to control potential toxic emissions including VOCs. Tax credits encouraging the use of waste reduction methods or waste treatment technologies known to be most environmentally sound can function as an incentive not to pollute.

Taxes and restrictions on the land disposal of certain hazardous wastes and "waste-end" taxes on the generation of hazardous and municipal wastes are other indirect preventive measures designed both to decrease the volume of wastes produced and to increase the competitiveness of other waste management options. The waste-end tax approach should be supported and implemented.

The regulatory system is an important factor in shaping industrial decisions to control waste either before generation or after generation. The system should encourage industries to undertake waste prevention as an opportunity and a challenge for pollution control. VOC emissions from TSDFs may be reduced through physical and procedural means before they are handled or treated. Sludges and organic wastes that readily generate gases and leachate are known to contribute a significant amount of VOCs. Thus, liquids containing organic compounds in waste landfills should be controlled because of their potential to contaminate not only ambient air but also groundwater. Wastes within TSDFs can be segregated to allow effective reductions in VOCs.

CONTAINMENT CONTROL TECHNOLOGIES

Covers are used to control air emissions from a variety of processes found at POTWs and TSDFs, and can be either ventilated or nonventilated. Most facilities use nonvented covers for both economic and safety reasons. Many waste processes can have enough hydrocarbon emissions to be explosive when mixed with oxygen. Therefore, ventilating the cover may result in an explosive atmosphere. POTWs traditionally have associated covers with odor control, and most of these covers are force-ventilated to an odor control device. Cover options discussed in this section include fixed roof covers, rigid floating covers, flexible floating covers, fixed covers in contact with the liquid surface, air-supported structures, and floating hollow spheres.

Fixed Roof Covers

Waste treatment processes can be covered by buildings, domes, or process level covers. Buildings are usually manufactured from concrete, concrete masonry units (CMU), prefabricated metal, or wood. Domes are manufactured out of either aluminum or fiberglass reinforced plastic (FRP). Process level covers are usually manufactured from steel, aluminum, FRP, or concrete. This type of covering system can be actively vented, passively vented, or non-vented. Actively vented systems may require large and expensive emissions control devices on the ventilation exhaust air. Passively vented systems normally require smaller emissions control devices, but can have hazardous and/or corrosive conditions underneath the cover due to the potentially high head-space concentrations of process volatile compounds. Non-vented systems must have pressure/vacuum relief valves to relieve pressure or vacuum if the process liquid level changes (CARB, 1988; U.S. EPA, 1990). Many times fixed covers that are used in petroleum refinery applications use either nitrogen or methane as a purge gas, to prevent oxygen from entering the cover, to prevent the formation of explosive conditions under the cover. Most cover systems at domestic wastewater treatment plants are required by building codes to be actively vented, with both mechanically supplied make-up air and mechanically removed exhaust air. The ventilation rates, required by building codes, vary from 12 to 30 air changes per hour.

Buildings are normally used when there are multiple, small process units that need to be covered. Many times processes in buildings will have there own covers with the building acting as secondary containment. If the building is to be occupied, it is almost always actively vented to reduce the possibility of developing an explosive or toxic atmosphere inside. It is also common to have alarm systems in buildings to alert occupants of potentially hazardous conditions.

Dome systems can clear spans up to 400 feet and are either built in a geodesic dome or arch configuration, with either a circular or rectangular base. They are very popular for large diameter tanks. Aluminum geodesic dome systems cost between $15 and $50 per square foot, depending on size and environmental loadings (Gravette et al., 1989). FRP domes are usually built in an arch configuration. Domes usually can be lifted on and off the process units intact, to access major interior equipment, with only the base having to be disconnected.

Process level covers offer the least headspace above the process liquid, reducing the amount of ventilation air needed if actively vented. These types of covering systems are often incorporated into the process vessel or tank construction using the same material as the process vessel or tank. Examples include covered steel tanks, covered concrete tanks, covered FRP tanks. Large processes may have column supported roofs or covers. It is common to cover large concrete process tanks with either poured in place concrete, precast concrete, aluminum planks, FRP panels, or aluminum checker-plate.

Access to the process for process control and maintenance of interior mechanical equipment is always a concern in covered systems. Ports and hatches must be strategically placed to allow for the normal operation of the process. For heavy maintenance, the covering systems normally have large removable sections.

Non-vented and passively vented systems must have nearly air-tight seals and seams to be effective. Actively vented systems normally withdraw enough air from the process to maintain less than atmospheric pressure under the cover, so that all leaks are into the system and not out of the system. Well sealed passive systems can reduce air emissions by up to 95% (Radian Corp., 1989). It is also essential to use soft rubber gaskets for all connections to maintain minimal emissions.

Rigid Floating Covers

Rigid floating covers control air emissions by floating on the process liquid surface. They are fabricated from either metal or plastic. Investigators have found that floating covers reduce air emissions by as much as 85% (CARB, 1988). Most losses occur from seams or at the process wall. This type of covering systems does not work well for processes that have large variations in liquid level or have solids that will interfere with the wall seal.

Typical applications of this covering system are the floating roof covers for hydrocarbon storage tanks and floating gas holding covers used for the anaerobic digestion of domestic wastewater solids. An equation has been developed by the American Petroleum Institute (API, 1989) to estimate the vapor loss from floating roof tanks. The equation is:

$$F = KV^n \tag{8-1}$$

where:
  K = rim seal loss factor
  V = average wind speed
  n = rim-seal-related wind-speed exponent

This equation only accounts for rim seal losses and does not estimate the losses from internal seams. For applications at oil refineries, the costs for rigid floating covers have been estimated at $42 per square foot, including site preparation and design.

Flexible Floating Covers

This type of cover is generally a flexible membrane that floats on the liquid surface. The membrane material is usually high density polyethylene (HDPE), but other thermoplastics can be used. One of the most common applications of this technology is in bulk volume fermentors, where high strength organic wastewater is anaerobically treated. These processes include gas collection systems to remove the methane that is generated during the process.

This type of cover can be used for most waste treatment processes, including hazardous waste treatment (Springer et al., 1985) but consideration must be made for access to interior equipment. The difficulty in accessing interior equipment normally mandates that interior equipment be kept to a minimum.

During the design of the cover system consideration must be made for the thermal expansion and contraction as well as rainwater collection and removal. In addition, covers can be damaged during high winds. The life expectancy of this type of covering system varies from 5 to 10 years. The cost for flexible floating covers range from $3 to $17 per square foot.

Fixed Covers in Contact with the Liquid Surface

This type of covering system can only be used where the water surface level is relatively constant. Essentially a cover of this type makes the process unit a pressure vessel. In order to assure that there is no vapor space under the cover a positive pressure of about 1 to 2 inches of water column is normally maintained in the vessel. This type of cover has not seen wide application.

Air Supported Structures

This type of structure consists of a flexible fabric that is inflated by blowers. Access to the cover is provided by airlocks. This type of structure is most commonly used to enclose outdoor tennis courts or ice rinks, but has been used for large hazardous waste remediation projects (U.S. EPA, 1990). Areas as large as 91 meters by 137 meters have been enclosed with this type of structure. When used for hazardous waste site remediation, the exhaust air has to be scrubbed to remove VOCs and toxic compounds.

The atmosphere inside air supported structures can be both hazardous and corrosive. In addition, in southern latitudes, the temperature inside the cover can reach 120°F during the daytime due to solar heat gain. These conditions make working inside the cover very difficult. As an example, it has been reported that the maintenance time required for equipment under the cover increases by a factor of 4 (Joffe, 1990). Often, self-contained breathing apparatus is required when working inside the structure. The air locks must be designed big enough that the internal equipment can be removed. This often increases cover cost.

It is also hazardous to work inside the cover during high winds or thunderstorms. If the cover collapses, workers may be trapped inside. Normally emergency power must be provided so that the cover will remain inflated during power failures.

A 4,000 m^2 cover will require a total of 26 Kw to maintain pressure in the structure. In addition, there are energy requirements for the exhaust air pollution control devices and temperature/humidity control, if provided. The structure costs between $54 and $65 per square meter.

Floating Spheres

This type of covering system is most commonly used to reduce emissions and heat loss from metal finishing tanks, however, they have been used to reduce emissions from static crude oil tanks (Springer et al., 1985). The reported efficiency is between 70 and 90 percent. For uniform sized spheres, the theoretical maximum coverage is 91%. This can be increased by using different sized spheres.

Provision must be made to inhibit sphere rotation, or emissions might actually increase over the emissions expected from an open tank. Wind, or tank turbulence, can induce the spheres to rotate. This type of covering system would be incompatible with processes that require mixing, skimming, or aeration. In addition, provision has to be made to assure that the spheres do not leave the tank with the waste being treated.

TREATMENT PROCESS
SELECTION/MODIFICATION
CONTROL TECHNOLOGIES

The amount of air emissions at a waste treatment facility is dependent on what type of waste treatment processes are used and the details of how those processes are designed, built, and operated. This section discusses some of the factors that affect volatilization and how air emissions can be reduced by process selection and/or modification.

Turbulence Control

For liquids processes at waste treatment facilities, air emissions are associated with points of turbulence. Major sources of air emissions from liquids processes are equalization basins, mixing, aeration basins, trickling filters, pre-aeration, aerated grit chambers, weirs, flumes, and drops. The following paragraphs describe some of the techniques available to achieve the same process objectives with less turbulence.

Weirs can be designed to reduce or eliminate turbulence. In general, the lower the weir drop is, the less volatilization there is of liquid phase compounds. Also, dropping directly into the receiving stream without intermediate splash points reduces air emissions. The lowest air emissions type of weir is a submerged weir, which consists of a submerged pipe with uniformly spaced orifices. The tailwater downstream of the pipe usually requires a mechanical level control device such as a butterfly gate or a valve controlled by an upstream level indicator.

In general, surface aerators have the highest air emissions; and almost all volatile compounds will be stripped in surface aeration systems. Trickling filters normally strip about 70 to 80% of the influent volatiles. Stripping can be reduced by force-ventilating the filter in a downdraft mode. Coarse-bubble diffused aeration systems strip out 30 to 80% of the volatiles, depending on compound volatility and the air rate. Plug flow systems with tapered aeration emit the highest percentage of volatiles. Fine-bubble diffused aeration systems strip out 20 to 50% of the volatiles, but highly volatile compounds such as 1,3-butadiene and carbon tetrachloride actually are stripped better in fine-bubble systems than in coarse-bubble systems. Most compounds such as chloroform and benzene are stripped proportionally to the air rate, so they are stripped significantly less in fine-bubble systems than in coarse-bubble systems. High-purity oxygen systems have the lowest stripping of the aeration processes, stripping between 1 and 15% of the volatiles.

Liquid Treatment Processes That
Can Reduce Emissions

Powdered Activated Carbon Activated Sludge
The literature shows that this is a very viable technology for enhancing the removal of toxic compounds in the liquid phase. It was found that

powdered activated carbon activated sludge systems were very effective at enhancing the removal of toxic substances present in wastewater streams. PAC activated sludge system doubled the removal of poorly degraded compounds compared with conventional activated sludge systems and removed 69 to 94% of compounds that had no degradation in activated sludge systems (Weber and Jones, 1986).

Chemical Oxidation and Photo-oxidation

Although there is literature available on chemical oxidation and photo-oxidation of toxics in water and wastewater (WPCF, 1985), it has been determined that oxidation is not cost-effective in liquid streams with a high biodegradable organic content, the situation at most wastewater treatment facilities. Therefore, it is not considered to be a viable process for liquid phase control.

Fly Ash

Fly ash from coal-fired power generation systems has some adsorption properties. Xylene was found to be the most readily adsorbable VOC with a removal of about 37% and a capacity of 1.3 mg/g of fly ash (Banerjee et al., 1988). The cost and disposal problems of the waste fly ash do not make this technology a leading candidate at this time.

VAPOR PHASE ADSORPTION

Although there are many adsorbent materials, the material that is overwhelmingly used for vapor phase air pollution control is granular activated carbon. Adsorption systems, using activated carbon, are normally regarded as best available control technology (BACT) by most air regulatory agencies for most volatile organic or air toxic compounds. This technology is most applicable on air streams that are below the economic threshold for thermal oxidation. EPA (U.S. EPA, 1986) suggests that the appropriate air stream characteristics for this technology are a concentration range of 1,000 to 10,000 ppmv, lower explosive limit of less than 25%, flow rates between 300 and 100,000 cfm, temperature less than 200°F, and the molecular weight of the target compounds between 45 and 130.

There are many circumstances where the compounds of concern are poorly adsorbed onto the carbon. The economic range of this technology can be extended by using in-situ regenerated systems. These systems usually use steam or hot air to desorb the material and then either discharge or reuse it in the liquid phase or thermally oxidize it in the gas phase. Other than the systems that use incinerators to destroy the desorb cycle air system, these systems have no local combustion emissions, like

NO_x and CO. However, the initial activation of the carbon and any subsequent thermal regeneration will have associated combustion emissions.

Adsorption Fundamentals

Gas phase adsorption processes can be used to separate a wide range of materials from process air streams. Normally adsorption processes are considered for use when the contaminant is fairly dilute in the air stream. Adsorbents may be polar or non-polar, however, polar sorbents will have a high affinity for water vapor and will be ineffective in air streams that have any appreciable humidity. Most air streams associated with waste treatment will be humid or even saturated with water vapor. Activated carbon, a non-polar adsorbent, is effective at removing all but the most volatile compounds associated with waste treatment systems. Activated carbon, if not specially treated, is non-specific to compounds, so all compounds will be absorbed in proportion to their gas phase concentrations. However, they are generally retained on the bed in inverse proportion to their volatilities. Therefore, if compounds are present, but not desired to be removed, they will be removed anyway with the proportional reduction of adsorption sites available to the compounds of concern.

Activated carbon can be specially treated, or impregnated, to enhance the adsorption of some species. An example of this is the impregnation of activated carbon with caustic to enhance the adsorption of hydrogen sulfide. Non-impregnated carbon has an adsorptive capacity for hydrogen sulfide of less than 1% by weight. Impregnated carbon can adsorb 20% by weight or more. However, the impregnant itself takes up sites, reducing the capacity of the carbon for non-acid components. Bromine has also been identified as an effective impregnant to enhance the adsorption of ethylene. In addition, it has also been reported that the injection of ammonia in a gas stream will increase the removal of hydrogen sulfide on activated carbon (Pope and Lauria, 1989).

When using non-polar adsorbents, there are two mechanisms that control the adsorption process, van der Waals forces and chemical bonding. Adsorption normally results in a decrease in free energy of the system making the reaction exothermic. This energy release can be substantial, resulting in auto-ignition of the activated carbon in extreme cases. Activated carbon can also act as a catalyst, promoting oxidation of some compounds after adsorption occurs, providing that oxygen is present.

Adsorption System Configurations

Several principles must be taken into consideration when designing carbon adsorption systems (Crocker and Schnelle, 1980):

- Allowing adequate contact time between the gas stream and the adsorption bed to ensure highest removal efficiency.
- Allowing adequate bed capacity to provide for a reasonable service cycle.
- Providing for minimum pressure drop through the adsorption system.
- Providing uniform gas distribution throughout the bed.
- Preparation of the gas stream to pre-cool or to remove particulate and other interfering components.
- Providing for the regeneration or bed replacement after the service cycle.

Adsorption systems can either be in a fixed, moving, or a fluidized bed. Fixed bed systems are by far the most popular. Most wastewater treatment activated carbon odor control systems consist of one to three beds in a fiberglass vessel. The beds are normally one to three feet deep. Typical gas face velocities range from 35 to 75 feet per minute. Carbon granule size is normally 4 × 6 mesh. These systems normally have an adsorption cycle of three months to three years. After the adsorption cycle the carbon is removed and either disposed of or taken to an off-site thermal regeneration facility. Impregnated carbon may be in-situ regenerated with caustic. However, this only is successful a portion of the time, due to tendency for most organic compounds to not respond to chemical regeneration. Impregnated carbon is normally not thermally regenerated due to the corrosive effects on the thermal regeneration system.

Fixed bed carbon systems can also be configured in metal enclosures, however the interior is subject to a very corrosive environment. Many small systems use a carbon bed fabricated from a 55 gallon steel drum. This is the typical system for passive vents on small tanks.

Fixed carbon beds can be in-situ regenerated by a variety of techniques. The most popular is a thermal swing system using hot air. An example of this type of system is shown in Figure 8-1. In this system there are several adsorption beds with the majority in operation in the adsorption mode. Normally one bed at a time is taken off-line and desorbed using hot air. The hot air is then taken to a gas incinerator where it is thermally oxidized. The incinerator off-gas is then used to heat the regeneration air. The system cycles in this manner continuously regenerating all the beds on the system. This type of system works best with gas streams that have few contaminants that are chemically similar, where all the compounds in the air stream will be thermally desorbed. In complex gas streams, there are often compounds that will not desorb at the temperatures normally used by these systems (400°F).

Steam can also be used as the regeneration gas. This type of system is normally used where there will be an attempt to recover the contaminant

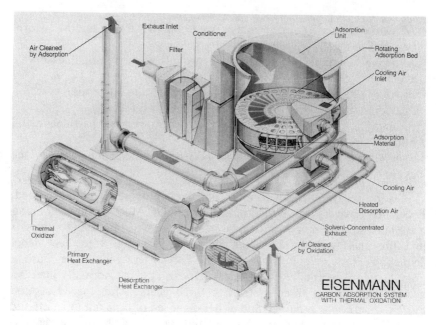

Air Cleaned by Adsorption

Exhaust Inlet

Conditioner

Filter

Adsorption Unit

Rotating Adsorption Bed

Cooling Air Inlet

Adsorption Material

Cooling Air

Heated Desorption Air

Solvent-Concentrated Exhaust

Air Cleaned by Oxidation

Thermal Oxidizer

Primary Heat Exchanger

Desorption Heat Exchanger

EISENMANN
CARBON ADSORPTION SYSTEM
WITH THERMAL OXIDATION

FIGURE 8-1.   An example of an activated carbon adsorption system utilizing in situ thermal swing regeneration with thermal destruction of regeneration gases.   (Courtesy of Eisenmann.)

for reuse. The steam is condensed after traveling through the bed and the condensate will contain the contaminates that the bed removed.

Beds can also be physically regenerated using a pressure swing or by stripping using a 'clean' gas stream. These techniques are generally only used for highly specialized applications. In addition, beds can be regenerated either chemically or biologically. The most prevalent case of chemical regeneration is in the odor control application described above. This works best on streams that have high proportions of the target compound. Biological regeneration has been demonstrated, but is not used commercially at this time.

Moving bed systems are often used where carbon is going to be in situ thermally regenerated. The bed is in a wheel configuration where it slowly turns between an adsorption cycle in the process air stream and a desorption cycle in a hot gas stream.

Fluidized bed systems utilize high gas velocity to fluidize the bed to improve mass transfer. However, since the adsorption zone is not fixed, these systems will have lower removal rates. This system is often used where there is a relatively high contaminant concentration and the highest removal levels are not required. Activated carbon in the fluid bed is normally continually removed for regeneration outside the adsorption vessel.

Interferences and Operating Problems

Although very high removal rates, up to 99.99%, can be achieved with activated carbon, most systems are only designed to remove between 90% and 95%. These lower removal rates are due to high air rates and allowing the bed to operate after the end of the adsorption zone has passed the bed. The EPA (U.S. EPA, 1986) presented the following anticipated removal efficiencies:

- 200–400 ppmv: 50%
- 1,000–2,000 ppmv: 95%
- 5,000–10,000 ppmv: 99%

High humidity in gas streams can effect the performance of adsorption systems. If the gas stream is close to saturation (above 80% relative humidity) capillary condensation can occur that both occupies potential adsorption sites and blocks access to the carbon pores. It may take air with a relative humidity of below 40% to remove this condensed water vapor (Crocker and Schnelle, 1980). Other problems can occur if there is particulate, or condensed oil or grease, that will blind the bed. Occasionally, inorganic precipitates can clog the bed of caustic impregnated carbon.

Since adsorption is an exothermic reaction, the adsorption of concentrated streams can result in bed temperatures in excess of the ignition point of the carbon. This normally will not occur unless 25% of the lower explosive limit is exceeded. In addition, for beds impregnated with caustic, there have been instances where the adsorption of oxygen onto the bed has caused the bed to exceed the carbon ignition temperature. Activated carbon can be prepared by bringing it in equilibrium with oxygen before it is shipped to reduce the possibility of a bed excursion. However, carbon beds should always be designed with the potential of fire in mind. They should be placed in areas with few combustible materials with good ventilation.

Carbon beds can be regenerated by both thermal swings and concentration swings. Therefore if the gas temperature or concentration changes, more contaminant may be released from the bed than adsorbed. For gas streams with large concentration changes, carbon beds tend to act like reservoirs that allow a constant contaminant stream out. This constant concentration gas stream out can often be higher in concentration than the concentration in, when the concentration in is at its lowest level. The same is true if the gas stream increases in temperature. Even relatively small changes in gas stream temperature can desorb significant amounts of some compounds.

Typical System Costs

Costs for activated carbon can be quite variable. They are a function of adsorption time, construction materials, volumetric flow rate, mass loadings, carbon capacity, and regeneration/disposal strategy.

Typical capital costs for fixed bed systems used for odor control are about $100,000 to $150,000 for a 10,000 cfm system. The costs are dependent on whether impregnated or non-impregnated carbon is used. This cost includes a fiberglass dual-bed vessel and fan. Replacement carbon costs between $1.00 and $1.50 per pound for non-impregnated carbon, and between $2.00 and $4.00 per pound for impregnated carbon. Energy costs will include fan power to overcome about 3 to 5 inches of water column head loss through the bed. In addition, if the stream is to be dehumidified, that cost can be substantial.

Thermal swing, in situ, regenerated systems cost about $475,000 for a 10,000 cfm system (U.S. EPA, 1978). This value was adjusted to 1992 dollars using the *Engineering News Record* cost index. Operation and maintenance costs were estimated to be $250,000. This cost is fairly independent of gas stream concentration. In fact it is possible that a higher concentration stream may be cheaper due to the combustion heat value in the off-gas.

THERMAL OXIDATION

Thermal oxidation can take place in either a fume incinerator or a flare. Fume incinerators, also known as thermal oxidizers, or after-burners, contain the gas in a chamber for a controlled detention time at a controlled temperature. These systems normally operate with dilute gases that are not autogenous. An exception to this is the use of fume incinerators to burn gas generated by anaerobic digesters at domestic wastewater treatment facilities. Flares are normally unconfined and are used on gas streams that are autogenous. In addition, waste gases are often combusted as fuel in process heaters or boilers.

Fume incinerators usually consist of a refractory lined combustion chamber that has a 1 to 2 second detention time. The temperature is controlled by burning a supplemental fuel, usually natural gas, to between 800°F and 1,500°F. Normally fume incinerators are not used unless they have heat recovery systems. The two types of systems available are recuperative systems, that have a counter current or cross current heat exchanger that uses exhaust gas to heat the incoming air flow, or regenerative systems, that cycle the inlet and outlet gases across a ceramic bed to recover the combustion heat.

Recuperative systems typically use a shell and tube heat exchanger as shown in Figure 8-2. This technology has been generally available since 1945. Regenerative systems are newer (refined in the early 1980's) and can have higher thermal efficiencies. They also have a lot of moving parts and can have gas short circuiting problems. Regenerative systems consist of multiple ceramic chambers that are cycled from the exhaust stream to the inlet stream. The chambers are switched using automatic dampers. If the transition is not executed well, or if the dampers leak, there can be short circuiting of inlet gas out the exhaust stream. Even though the combustion efficiency of the incinerator can reach as high as 99.9% destruction, short circuiting can reduce this to as low as 90% (Murray et al., 1992).

Although most hydrocarbons will be completely destroyed when held at 1,400°F for 2 seconds, some chlorinated compounds require temperatures as high as 2,200°F. The design variables that control destruction are detention time, temperature, and degree of mixing in the combustion cham-

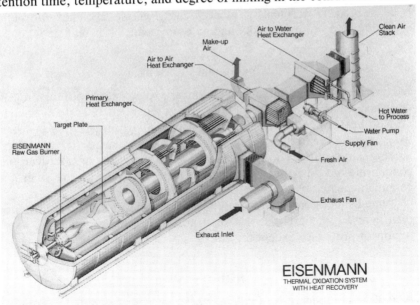

FIGURE 8-2.   An example of a thermal oxidation system with recuperative heat recovery.   (Courtesy of Eisenmann.)

ber (Rolke et al., 1972). Carbon monoxide inhibits the attainment of high destruction efficiencies when it is over 2,000 ppmv. Increased detention time will increase efficiency in this case. For inlet conditions ranging from 850 to 12,200 ppmv and temperatures from 1,160°F to 1,800°F destruction efficiencies have been reported to range from 70.3% to 99.9% (Blackburn et al., 1980).

If the gas stream is autogenous, then flares can be used to destroy the hydrocarbons. Flares can either be unshielded or shielded. Shielded flares are also called ground flares. Flares are shielded to protect personnel and equipment from the flare as well to reduce noise, smoke, and luminosity. Flare temperatures range from 1,400 to 2,500°F. They primary used to control hydrocarbon emissions from process upsets or emergencies. If the stream characteristics and flow can be controlled the gas is normally disposed of in a process heater or boiler to recover the heat value of the gas.

Flares generally have a pilot flame to assure that combustion is maintained. In addition, steam is also added to help mix the gases and to react with complex hydrocarbons. Flares have reported destruction efficiencies of 70% to 100%. Flare efficiency is dependent on flare head design and gas composition. Compounds that are destroyed by flares include acetaldehyde, acetic acid, acrolein, acrylic acid, acrylonitrile, cyclohexane, methanol, ethylene, formaldehyde, and chloromethanes (Shareef, 1984).

Operational Concerns

Recuperative systems have a much longer experience record than regenerative systems. Most of the problems with recuperative systems have to do with heat exchanger fouling and heat exchanger integrity. Regenerative systems have fairly complicated control requirements and have many moving parts. In addition, there have been instances of hydrocarbons condensing out on the cold ceramic and then catching on fire when the ceramic is heated by the combustion gases.

Fume incinerators will inherently have a higher destruction efficiency than flares. In general flares should not be considered for most waste treatment processes except for emergency or upset conditions.

System Costs

A 50,000 cfm recuperative fume incinerator was reported to cost between $600,000 and $800,000 with 50% heat recovery (Shen et al., 1990). The cost of flare systems are substantially less but difficult to quantify because of the wide range of types and applications.

CATALYTIC THERMAL OXIDATION

Fume incinerators that use a catalyst bed can effectively fully oxidize many organic compounds at temperatures that are far lower than conventional fume incinerators. These systems operate at temperatures in the 700 to 900°F range and are normally used only on dilute gas streams, under 25% of the lower explosive limit.

Catalyst beds come in many configurations and materials. Common materials include noble metals (platinum, palladium, and rhodium), copper chromite, copper oxides, chromium oxides, manganese oxides, nickel oxides, and cobalt oxides. Beds can be configured in either fixed or fluid bed systems. The catalyst will abrade in fluid bed systems, which can be an advantage if the application tends to foul or deactivate the catalyst. Fixed bed catalysts can be in a loose bead configuration or a fixed structure such as a ceramic or metal honeycomb, or as a ceramic rod. The ceramic rod systems usually have the lowest pressure drop.

Packaged units are available for applications ranging from 100 to 100,000 cfm. There are several major manufacturers. Most organic compounds are efficiently removed in catalytic systems. Typical destruction efficiencies are about 95%, however, most systems can be designed to obtain over 99% at an increased cost due to high operating temperatures and large catalyst beds. Compounds that have been successfully removed by catalytic systems include olefins, aromatics, oxygenated organics, organic nitrogen compounds, and chlorinated hydrocarbons. Typical inlet concentrations range from 100 to 2,000 ppmv (Kosuko and Ramsey, 1988; U.S. EPA, 1978).

Operational Concerns

Catalysts can be plugged with particulate or condensate. In addition the bed can be deactivated by sulfur compounds or chlorinated hydrocarbons (Green and Nunez, 1990; Rolke et al., 1972). Catalysts are being developed that are tolerant of these conditions and they can be somewhat mitigated by operating at a higher temperature. However, bed longevity is normally inversely proportional to operating temperature. Catalysts normally last between 2 and 5 years. Unless there has been substantial previous experience with catalytic systems on a VOC stream, it is recommended that the system be extensively pilot tested to determine correct catalyst type and to develop appropriate control strategies for the full scale system.

One of the concerns about operating catalytic systems on gas streams that have a variable VOC concentration is the control of bed temperature.

If the bed temperature exceeds the maximum design temperature, the catalyst will irreversibly deactivate, and the catalysis bed is normally one of the most expensive components of the system. In addition, if the lower explosion limit is exceeded, the bed may explode. Most systems are equipped with hydrocarbon monitoring devices to prevent either of these situations from occurring.

Since catalytic systems operate at relatively low temperatures they normally have lower NO_x emissions than other thermal technologies. However, they still will produce acid gas emissions, like HCl, that may need to be scrubbed.

System Costs

The cost for a 50,000 cfm catalytic system was reported to be between $1,000,000 and $1,500,000 (Shen et al., 1990). The major operational cost will be the heating of the gas stream to the bed operating temperature.

CONVENTIONAL WASTEWATER ODOR CONTROL SYSTEM TECHNOLOGIES

This section discusses the potential for wastewater treatment odor control technology to control emissions from waste treatment processes other than odor. Most odor control at wastewater treatment facilities focuses on hydrogen sulfide and a selection of odor-causing but not necessarily toxic organic compounds. In some instances, ammonia also is of concern. The focus here will not be on odor but on the ability of these technologies to control emissions that may be of concern but do not necessarily present an odor problem. These compounds are primarily toxics and reactive organic gas (ROG).

Vapor phase odor control technology includes dry scrubbing systems, wet scrubbing systems, and biological scrubbing systems. These technologies control a fairly broad spectrum of compounds. Substances said to be controlled in wastewater odor control devices that may be of interest in other waste treatment facilities include ammonia, total organic vapor, toluene, methyl mercaptan, ROG and non-ROG hydrocarbons, styrene, acrolein, acetaldehyde, p-dichlorophenol, and general priority pollutants (Card, 1989; Lovett and Poltarek, 1974; Luebke, 1989; Morton and Card, 1987; Patterson et al., 1984; Posselt and Reidies, 1965; Sohr, 1975).

In addition to controlling air pollutants, some technologies are suspected of producing pollutants. Two-stage acid/alkali packed tower systems appear to produce chlorinated hydrocarbons (Card, 1989). High concentrations of methylene chloride have been found in the exhaust of a two-stage sodium hypochlorite/sodium hydroxide packed tower system (Shahalam, 1982). Also, some proprietary organic scrubbing solutions have unknown compositions that may contain or produce toxics (Duffee, 1988).

Atomized mist systems were reported to remove between 89 and 98% of toxic organic compounds; single-stage packed tower systems removed about 50% (Card, 1989). Methyl mercaptan removal of up to 80% was reported in a packed tower that was removing over 99% of the hydrogen sulfide (Luebke, 1989).

A packed tower system was reported to have removed total organic vapor from 0.495 ppm to 0.181 ppm (Patterson et al., 1984). A potassium permanganate packed tower was found to remove over 95% ROG and 50% non-ROG hydrocarbon (Sohr, 1975). In another potassium permanganate system it was found that 99.5% styrene, 99.99% acrolein, 85% acetaldehyde, and 80% p-dichlorophenol were removed (Posselt and Reidies, 1965). Nonquantitatively, it was found that a caustic scrubber did not remove a solvent odor (Beardsly et al., 1958).

Some anomalies in the literature, such as water-based liquid scrubbing systems removing non-water-soluble compounds and removal rates that are independent of traditional partition values, have not been fully explained (Card, 1989). As this behavior is not fully understood, there could very well be unknown interferences.

Costs for these technologies vary with size and odor strength. The cost range (present worth) is between $0.30 and $20.00/lb of hydrogen sulfide removed (ASCE, 1989). The lower-cost systems are air injection and scrubbing with liquid scrubbers. For large air flows, the highest-cost system on a hydrogen sulfide removal basis is activated carbon. However, for smaller applications and dilute air streams, activated carbon systems can be cheaper. Larger liquid scrubbing systems (over 10,000 cfm) with modest odor levels, 25 ppm or less of hydrogen sulfide equivalent, cost between $10 and $30 per installed cfm on a present worth basis (ASCE, 1989; U.S. EPA, 1985b).

EMERGING EMISSIONS
CONTROL TECHNOLOGIES

Biofiltration

Biofiltration has been used extensively to control odors at wastewater treatment facilities. However, most of these control systems are quite small, less than 5,000 cfm. There is considerably more application of this technology in Europe and Asia than North America. There are some systems in Europe that are designed specifically for the control VOCs and even air toxics (Ottengraf et al., 1984b). In North America there have been two types of systems that have been popular. The first, a compost filter or soil filter, has been used to control odors mostly at composting facilities and small pump stations. This technology consists of an air distribution system underneath a bed of compost or soil. A second technology consists of a device almost identical to a wastewater treatment biofilter that uses attached growth to bioconvert wastewater organics. Odorous gases are introduced into the bottom of this structure and exhausted at the top. Primary treated wastewater is circulated over the top through artificial media that has attached biological growth. Both of these systems have had a checkered past. Most of the small systems that treat lightly contaminated gas streams work successfully. Most of the large systems that treat concentrated odorous streams do not work well. An exception to this is the use of activated sludge aeration basins as vapor phase control devices. This technology effectively removes even concentrated odors at air flow rates as high as 170,000 cfm. However this technology is not cost competitive unless the system is primarily used to treat the wastewater.

In this book, biological vapor phase control devices that utilize compost, peat, bark, soil, or other media that is close packed and not constantly irrigated is termed a biofilter. Control devices that are constantly irrigated and loose-packed, or are gas-dispersed-in-liquid systems are termed bioscrubbers. In biofilters the media serves as a physical support and as an additional food source. Contaminants are first adsorbed to the media and then biotransformed by the organisms to non-volatile or inorganic compounds. Water is normally required to sustain the biological population and to maintain optimum air flow characteristics.

Some of the compounds that have been reported to have been removed by biofilters include hydrogen sulfide, mercaptans, terpenes, amines, benzene, toluene, xylene, styrene, ethylbenzene, propane, n-butane, ethylacetate, butylacetate, butanol, trichloroethene, tetrachloroethene, and chlorobenzene. Removal efficiencies have reported to range from 69% to 99% (Alexander, 1981; Bohn, 1989; Eitner, 1989; Hartenstein, 1987; Kampbell et al., 1987; Kosky and Neff, 1988; McCarty, 1988; Ottengraf et al., 1984a).

Biofilters can require large areas. Most biofilter design face velocities range between 2 and 8 feet per minute. At a face velocity of 2 feet per minute, a 100,000 cfm scrubber would take over an acre of land area. However, the process cover system could have an integral biofilter built into it, so additional site area need not be used.

The most important design considerations for biofilters are the media type, moisture control, and air distribution. Most failures are attributed to poor air distribution and/or media blinding or breakthrough due to poor moisture control. Biofilters that scrub large amounts of acid gases, specifically hydrogen sulfide can develop pH problems in the biofilter. This can be mitigated by adding a buffer material (oyster shells or limestone) to the bed, or by prescrubbing the acid gas before it gets to the biofilter. Since biofilters are biological systems they require acclimation and a consistent food source. Acclimation periods are normally about 1 month. Biofilters have been reported to survive at least 2 weeks while being inactive. When constructing biofilters in northern climates, care must be taken to assure that the biofilter remains warm enough to sustain biological activity and that the top of the filter does not blind by freezing. Most northern climate biofilters are completely enclosed to retain heat.

Biofilter costs were estimated by the EPA to be about $100,000 for a 10,000 cfm system that was designed to remove 20 ppm of hydrogen sulfide to less than 1 ppm (Neff, 1988). Annual operating costs were estimated to be about $8,000 per year. The capital cost is comparable to most odor control equipment, including packed tower scrubbers and activated carbon scrubbers.

UV/Ozone/Hydrogen Peroxide/Catalysis

Ozone has been used for several years as a gas phase odor control technology. Ultraviolet light has been tested for application in odor control, but is not in general use. Both of these are powerful oxidants by themselves and yet more powerful when used in combination. At this time there are no significant activities to use these technologies to control VOCs in the gas phase.

One unique instance of the use of this technology is a project where the U.S. Air Force in conjunction with EPA studied the use of this technology for an application of VOC removal from a contaminated groundwater source (Ashworth et al., 1987). Ultrox International was contracted to test their liquid phase advanced oxidation process that uses a combination of UV, ozone, and hydrogen peroxide. One concern during the design of the test was the stripping of organics instead of oxidizing them. In order to reduce the tendency for the VOCs to escape in the off-gas, Ultrox developed a combination catalytic ozone destruct system and UV light source. The UV light was intended to destroy any vapor phase organic compounds that escaped the liquid phase.

The device tested was a Decompozon unit supplied by Ultrox International. This unit was designed with a nickel based proprietary catalyst to decompose ozone coupled with a UV light source for the destruction of vapor phase organic compounds. The unit destroyed 99% of the dichloroethene and trichloroethene, but only destroyed 75% of the total organics. Additional tests were conducted at other locations and the unit reported to function well but removals were not quantified (Barich and Zeff, 1990).

Membrane Processes

Membranes have been used to separate gas phase components for several years, however none has been used to separate VOCs from waste treatment process off-gas. The most promising application for membranes as a strategy to reduce air emissions is to use a membrane to introduce oxygen into a waste stream instead of a diffuser or surface aerator. Another application is where a membrane is used to support a biological growth, with the organism's oxygen supply coming from inside the membrane. A proposed, but never investigated, strategy is to use a membrane to separate VOCs in the liquid blowdown of a high interface area scrubber. The scrubber water could then be recycled and the VOCs removed in a concentrated liquid stream. At this time membrane technology is only a curiosity for the application of controlling VOC emissions from waste treatment processes.

AIR EMISSIONS CONTROL
DURING REMEDIATION

Many specialized technologies are available for air emissions control during remediation of uncontrolled hazardous waste sites. The uniqueness of each site demands that careful selection be made for control technologies. Because emission mechanisms and rates are so highly variable during remediation, selection of the control technology must be based on the information developed during the air pathway analysis and emissions estimation phases.

The control methods for dust and vapor suppression rarely remove 100% of the contaminants from the air. Some methods have very limited periods of effectiveness, making multiple applications or specialized formulations necessary. Table 8-1 summarizes the control technologies available for remediation, and Table 8-2 presents relative costs.

Soil Vapor Pore Volume Reduction

Volatilization of contaminants from a hazardous waste site may be controlled by reducing the soil vapor pore volume (U.S. EPA, 1984). The rate of volatilization can be reduced by adding water to reduce the air-filled

TABLE 8-1.   Summary of VOC air emissions control technologies for site remediation.

Control	Advantages	Disadvantages
Foams	Easy to apply Effective Allows for the control of working faces Can reduce decontamination	Moderately expensive Requires trained operators
Complete enclosure/ treatment system	May provide the highest degree of control for some applications	High cost Air scrubbing required High potential risk Must work in enclosure
Fill material	Inexpensive Equipment usually available	Hard to seal airtight No control for working face Creates more contaminated soil
Synthetic membrane	Simple approach	Worker contact with waste during application Hard to seal airtight
Aerodynamic modification	Simple Lower cost Low maintenance	Variable control Requires additional controls
Fugitive VC/PM collection systems	Can be used in active areas	Limited operational data exist Effective range limited Maintenance required
Minimizing surface area	Inexpensive Can be included in plan	Must maintain Cannot always dictate size
Water	Easy to apply	A potential exists for groundwater contamination
Inorganic/organic control agents	Similar to foams	Not as effective as foams for working areas

Source: Radian Corporation, 1987.

pore spaces or by reduction of the spaces themselves through compaction techniques. Compaction or water addition will displace the volatiles occupying the free spaces, resulting in soil venting. Also, water suppression might result in mobilizing the contaminant into a groundwater medium if not properly applied. Wastes amenable to this form of suppression include most volatile organic and inorganic compounds in soil. Contami-

TABLE 8-2.   Relative effectiveness and costs for remediation air emission control technologies.

Suppression Technique	Relative Effectiveness			Relative Cost
	Low	Medium	High	
Minimizing waste surface area	+	+	+	1
Aerodynamic considerations	+			1
Wind screens	+			1
Wind blocks	+			1
Orientation of activities	+			1
Covers, mats, membranes, and fill	+	+		2–3
Water application	+	+		2–3
Water/additives	+	+		2–3
Inorganic control agents	+	+		2–3
Organic dust control		+		2–3
Foam suppressants		+	+	7–10
Enclosures			+	10

nants with a high vapor phase mobility and a low water phase partition potential are particularly amenable to this vapor control technique.

Physical/Chemical Barriers

Physical/chemical barriers have found broad utility in temporary vapor and particulate control from hazardous waste sites (U.S. EPA, 1985a). They include foams, wind screens, synthetic covers, and water/surfactant sprays. The application of foams during excavation operations and tarps for overnight storage can achieve a greater overall control efficiency at a significantly lower cost than the use of an enclosure with activated carbon vapor phase control.

REFERENCES

Alexander, M., 1981. Biodegradation of Chemicals of Environmental Concern. *Science,* Vol. 211, p. 132 (Jan. 9).

API, 1989. Evaporative Loss from External Floating Roof Tanks. API Publication 2517, third edition.

ASCE, 1989. Sulfide Control in Wastewater Collection and Treatment Systems. MOP No. 69.

Ashworth, R. A., et al., 1987. Destruction of Organic Contaminants by Catalytic Oxidation. EPA/600/D-87/224.

Banerjee, K., et al., 1987. Sorption of Selected Organic Pollutants by Fly Ash. *Proceedings* of the 43rd IWC, Purdue University.

Barich, J. T., and Zeff, J. D., 1990. Commercial Applications of ULTROX Ultraviolet/Oxidation Technology at Municipal and Industrial Groundwater Superfund Sites. *Proceedings* of the 83rd AWMA Meeting.

Beardsly, C. W., et al., 1958. Removal of Sewer Odors by Scrubbing with Alkaline Solutions. *Sewage Works Journal*, p. 30.

Blackburn, J. W., et al. 1980. Organic Chemical Manufacturing, Vol. 4—Combustion Control Devices. EPA-450/3-80-026, PB81-220535.

Bohn, H. L., 1989. VOC Removal by Soil Filter Beds. *Proceedings* of HAZMACON.

California Air Resources Board (CARB), 1988. Suggested Control Measure for the Control of Organic Compound Emissions from Sumps Used in Oil Production.

Card, T. R., 1989. Volatile Organic Compound Removal in Packed Towers and Atomized Mist Odor Scrubbing Systems. Presented at the 62nd WPCF.

Crocker, B. B., and K. B. Schnelle, Jr., 1980. Control of Gases by Absorption, Adsorption, and Condensation. *Handbook of Air Pollution Control Technology*, Chapter 7. John Wiley & Sons, New York.

Duffee, R. A., 1988. DeAmine Odor Tests Results. Odor Science and Engineering, Inc.

Eitner, D., 1989. Biofilter in Flue Gas Cleaning: Biomasses, Design, Costs, and Applications. Brennst-Waerme-Kraft (German), 41/3, L24.

Federal Register, July 22, 1991. Hazardous Waste TSDF: Organic Air Emission Standards for Tanks, Surface Impoundments, and Containers, pp. 33505–33509.

Gravette, B., et al., "An Overview of Odor Control Systems." Presented at the 1989 Pacific Northwest Water Pollution Control Association Conference.

Green, H. L., and C. M. Nunez, 1990. Deactivation by H_2S and Cr_2O_3 Emission Control Catalyst for Chlorinated VOC Destruction. Presented at the 83rd AWMA.

Hartenstein, H., 1987. Assessment and Redesign of an Existing Biofiltration System. M.S. thesis, Dept. of Env. Eng. Sc., University of Florida, Gainesville, FL.

Joffe, L. B., 1990. Use of an Air-Inflated Dome to Control VOC Emissions from an Aeration Lagoon. *Environmental Progress*, Vol. 9, p. 2 (May).

Kampbell, D. H., et al., 1987. Removal of Aliphatic Hydrocarbons in a Soil Bioreactor. *JAPCA*, Vol. 37, No. 10, p. 1236 (Oct.).

Kosky, J., and C. R. Neff, 1988. Innovative Biological System for Hydrocarbon Treatment. Biofilter Technology for Air Toxics Emissions at POTWs. Biofiltration Inc., Gainesville, FL.

Kosusko, M., and G. M. Ramsey, 1988. Destruction of Air Emissions Using Catalytic Oxidation. EPA/600/D-88/107.

Lovett, W. D., and R. Poltarak, 1974. Activated Carbon Used to Control Odors. *Water and Sewage Works*, Vol. 121, p. 8.

Luebke, E. M., 1989. Gurnee, Illinois Odor Report. Illinois Institute of Technology Research Institute.

McCarty, P., 1988. Bioengineering Issues Related to In Situ Remediation of Contaminated Soils and Groundwater. *Environmental Technology*, Omenn, Editor, Plenum Publishing Corp., New York.

Morton, C., and T. Card, 1987. Design of Packed Towers for Odor Control. Presented at the 60th WPCF.

Murray, C. M., et al., "Regenerative Thermal Oxidation for the Control of Biosolids Compost Odor." Presented at the 1992 Water Environment Federation Conference.

Neff, C. R., 1988. Biofilter Technology for Odor Control. Biofilter Technology for Air Toxics Emissions at POTWs. Biofiltration Inc., Gainesville, FL.

Ottengraf, S. P. P., and A. H. C. Van Den Oever, 1984a. Kinetics of Organic Compounds Removal from Waste Gases with a Biological Filter. *Biotechnology and Bioengineering*, Vol. 25, p. 3089.

Ottengraf, S. P. P., et al., 1984b. Waste Gas Purification in a Biological Filter Bed. *Prog. Ind. Microbiol.*, Vol. 20, p. 157.

Ottengraf, S. P. P., et al., 1986. Biological Elimination of Volatile Xenobiotic Compounds in Biolfilters. *Bioprocess Engineering*, Vol. 1, p. 61.

Patterson, R. G., et al., 1984. Odor Controls for Sewage Treatment Facilities. Presented at the 77th APCA.

Pope, R. J., and J. M. Lauria, 1989. Odors: The Other Effluent. *Civil Engineering*, p. 42 (Aug.).

Posselt, H. S., and A. H. Reidies, 1965. Odor Abatement with Potassium Permanganate Solutions. *I&EC Product Research and Development*.

Radian Corporation, 1989. Testing Fugitive VOC Emissions from an API Oil Separator at the Chevron, U.S.A., Inc. Richmond Refinery. WSPA Tech. Memo.

Rolke, R. W., et al., 1972. Afterburner System Study. EPA-R2-72-062.

Shahalam, A. B. M., 1982. Scrubbing Odors from Wastewater Treatment. *Journal of Environmental Engineering*, Vol. 108, p. 4.

Shareef, G. S., et al., 1984. Hazardous/Toxic Air Pollutant Control Technology: A Literature Review. EPA/6002/2084/194.

Shen, T. T., et al., "Assessment and Control of VOC Emissions from Waste Disposal Facilities." Critical Reviews in Environmental Control, Vol. 20, Issue 1. 1990.

Sohr, R. T., 1975. Removal of Hydrocarbons, Smoke, and Odor from Oil Bake Ovens Economically with Chemical Absorption. *AFS Transactions*.

Springer, C., et al., 1985. In Situ Methods to Control Emissions from Surface Impoundments and Landfills. EPA 600/2-85-124.

U.S. Environmental Protection Agency, 1978. Control Techniques for Volatile Organic Emissions from Stationary Sources. EPA-450/2-78-022 (May).

U.S. Environmental Protection Agency, 1985a. Handbook—Remedial Action at Waste Disposal Sites (Revised). EPA/626/6-85/006.

U.S. Environmental Protection Agency, 1985b. Odor and Corrosion Control in Sanitary Sewage Systems and Treatment Plants. EPA 625/1-85/018.

U.S. Environmental Protection Agency, 1986. Handbook of Control Technologies for Hazardous Air Pollutants. EPA/625/6-86/014 (Sept.).

U.S. Environmental Protection Agency, 1990. Industrial Wastewater Volatile Organic Compound Emissions—Background Information for BACT/LAER Determinations. EPA 450/3-0-004.

Weber, W. J., and B. E. Jones, 1986. Toxic Substance Removal in Activated Sludge and PAC Treatment Systems. EPA/600/S2-86/045 (June).

9

Summary and Conclusions

Only recently have atmospheric scientists, regulators, public health specialists, and the general public become aware of the presence and potential impact of volatile organic compounds in the environment. VOC emissions concerns include their role in human exposure to toxic compounds, nuisance odors, ozone formation, deterioration of the quality of life, and damage to ecological systems. For many reasons, these potentially toxic contaminants have gone unnoticed and largely unregulated while emphasis has been placed on the priority pollutants. That situation is changing, and assessment and control of VOC emissions now are relevant issues.

As VOC emission sources are varied, are widely dispersed, and often are difficult to assess, it is not surprising that this category of air contaminants has followed others in terms of assessment, regulation, and control. VOC emissions are waste stream and process–specific and are related to the level of VOC in the waste stream or the VOC emission source. The number of waste constituents falling into the category of VOC emissions is staggering. For instance, more than 4,000 compounds have been identified in municipal and industrial wastes, many of which are volatile; and subtle changes in waste composition and/or physical characteristics can significantly influence the VOC emissions from a given process or source.

Waste treatment process design and operational parameters will affect VOC emissions, resulting in unique VOC emissions per treatment process. About 90% by weight of industrial hazardous waste are generated in liquid streams, and 60% of these wastes are organic wastes. VOC emissions from these treatment processes occur through such mechanisms as volatilization, hydrolysis, photodecomposition, biodegradation, and incineration. These treatment processes may or may not have emission control devices.

Regulation and control of VOC emissions from waste treatment and disposal facilities is in its infancy. It is a compromise between the public health and welfare and technical, economic, and political factors. The most important and relevant laws governing VOC emission controls are the current RCRA, CERCLA, SARA, and, most important, CAA and the recent amendments. New regulations will follow VOC source assessments research.

The selection of the VOC emission assessment approach, technology, and sample collection/analytical technique will depend on several factors: the type of VOC emission source in question (point or area source), the type and the level of VOCs involved, the emission source characteristics, and the capabilities and resources available to conduct the VOC emission assessment. Whenever possible, measurement technologies, especially direct emission assessment technologies, should be used, such as vent sampling for point sources and surface flux chambers for area sources. Indirect emission assessment technologies are useful but often are limited by upwind interferences and meteorological conditions. Popular indirect technologies include upwind/downwind sampling using point monitors or the transect technique using point or line source monitoring. Optical remote sampling may prove to be most useful technology for point and area VOC emission sources, provided that the VOCs of interest are spectroscopically active, and optical remote equipment is available for the assessment. Likewise, fenceline monitoring may prove useful; however, an approach that requires modeling may not provide data that meets the assessment requirements of accuracy and precision. In some cases, an adequate assessment can be performed by using mathematical models to assess the VOC emissions potential of the source. Available capabilities including personnel, equipment, resources, and the schedule are all important considerations that will influence the selection of the most appropriate approach for the VOC emission assessment.

Mathematical models for air quality assessment consist of statistical models, emission-predictive models, and atmospheric dispersion models. Statistical models have been well developed and used for many years to assess emissions. Emission-predictive models are exclusively theoretical, and each model generally applies only to a specific waste source. Only limited field data are available to validate or verify predictive models; therefore, further research is needed for full utilization of emission-predictive models. The preferred atmospheric dispersion models have been presented, and this approach can produce credible screening or in-depth emission estimates. Often, the recommended method is to screen the

VOC emission source and then follow up the screening with a focused assessment using a measurement approach that will produce a highly accurate, precise, and representative emission assessment.

VOC pathway analysis is a systematic approach for conducting assessments of the nature and the extent of VOC emissions and how the VOCs interact with the environment and receptors. The analysis involves understanding VOC emission mechanisms, atmospheric processes, receptor exposure potential, and the assessment of adverse health effects resulting from the exposure. Thus, it is essential to know how the VOC is released and transported to the receptor and what transformations occur during transport. The risk assessments generally are linked to risk created by single compounds resulting in exposure in a simple medium. Environmental professionals are encouraged to assess the combined risk posed by one compound in several media or by interactions with other compounds.

Traditionally, VOC control strategies have been limited to the installation of add-on devices such as adsorption devices or condensation units to the ventilation systems of treatment processes. Recently, VOC controls have focused on the use of manifest systems, waste reduction reporting, toxic substance release inventories, waste recycling, and permit systems to provide steps and procedures designed to control potentially toxic VOC emissions. Ultimately, the use of preventive measures will be the most effective control strategy to minimize VOC emissions from waste treatment and disposal facilities. Preventive measures commonly used include waste reduction and recycling of wastes or pretreatment of waste streams with a significant VOC content.

In summary, several important considerations must be included in a strategy for assessing and controlling VOC emissions from any one of the variety of VOC emission sources previously discussed. There is a wide range of types and levels of VOC emission from those industrial, municipal, and hazardous waste treatment facilities (controlled and uncontrolled), and there is very little similarity between VOC emissions (rate and compound emissions) from these facilities/sources. This is so because of the diverse nature and composition of the wastes, and the variety of ways in which these wastes are handled. What is consistent, however, is the way in which VOC emissions are dealt with in terms of assessment and control.

The most critical component of assessing and controlling VOC emissions is the approach to this task, which starts with developing a thorough understanding of the VOC emission source. It is essential that there be a complete understanding of the source, which can be obtained only through a study of it resulting in knowledge of the chemical composition of waste streams/hazardous waste, waste stream composition changes as a function of process operation, treatment design and operation, and emission estimates for waste types and facility operation. Once the VOC source is well characterized and understood, then the need for control technologies can be evaluated. This typically is done by researching applicable regulations and comparing emissions per source to regulatory levels, or through health risk analysis and evaluation of the projected health risk. If control is required or recommended, feasible control technologies can be designed and used to control the emissions to acceptable VOC emission levels. Estimates of control efficiency applied to the VOC emission estimates then can be used with standard health risk assessment protocols to estimate the impact of the controlled VOC emission source on the surrounding environment and neighboring receptors. These controlled emission rate estimates and modeled impacts may be used to determine whether the source is in compliance with applicable regulations regarding VOC emissions.

Ultimately, the goal is to allow for the treatment and disposal of all forms of waste-containing VOCs in a way that meets health- and environment-based regulations and is a viable, cost-effective waste treatment and disposal option. Without proper study and then control of these VOC emissions, we are remiss as scientists, engineers, regulators, and manufacturers. With the tools and protocols provided in this book, we can begin to address these issues so that VOC emissions from the municipal, industrial, and waste treatment/disposal facilities can be designed, operated, and controlled to yield acceptable levels of VOC emissions.

Appendix A

Chemical and Physical Properties for 25 Compounds of Potential Concern

No.	Compound	Henry's Law Constant (atm-m/mol)	Henry's Law Constant (atm-m³/gmol)	Henry's Law Constant (atm) @20°C	log K_{OW} (octanol-water partition coeff) (@25°C)	Flash Point (°C)	Vapor Density	Maximum Water Solubility mg/l	V-L Equil. Constant K
1	Acetone		2.50E − 05		−0.24	−18	2	1000000	
2	Acrylonitrile	0.00550	8.80E − 05		−0.92	0	1.83	79000	
3	Benzene	0.03020	5.50E − 03	2.40E + 02	2.13 @ 20°C	−11	2.77	1750	61.9
4	Carbon tetrachloride	0.0039	3.00E − 02	1.29E + 03	2.83	nonflam	5.3	757	313.1
5	Chlorobenzene	0.0039	3.93E − 03		2.84 @ 20°C	23	3.88	466	40.8
6	Chloroform	0.0039	3.39E − 03	1.70E + 02	1.97 @ 20°C	nonflam	4.12	8200	49
7	Dichlorobenzene, o-		1.94E − 03		3.38	66	5.05	100	
	Dichlorobenzene, m-		3.61E − 03		3.38	63	5.08	123	
	Dichlorobenzene, p-		1.60E − 03		3.39	65.5	5.08	790	
8	1,1-Dichloroethane	0.0056	5.54E − 03	1.90E + 02	1.79	−5	3.44	5500	71.3
9	1,2-Dichloroethane	0.0014	1.20E − 03		1.48	13	3.4	8520	17.1
10	Ethylbenzene		6.44E − 03	6.10E + 01	3.15	15	3.66	152	
11	Isopropyl alcohol		1.50E − 04		−0.16/0.28 calc	12	2.07		
12	Methylene chloride	0.0032	2.24E − 03		1.25	nonflam	2.93	20000	49.8
13	Methyl ethyl ketone		4.35E − 05		0.26	−3	2.42	268000	
14	Methyl t-butyl ether		7.80E − 04		1.74 ± 0.12	−28	4.42		
15	Napthalene		1.18E − 03		3.01/3.45	88	3.24		
16	Phenol		4.54E − 07		1.46	79	5.83	93000	
17	Tetrachloroethylene		2.90E − 02	1.10E + 03	2.60 @ 20°C	nonflam	3.14	150	
18	Toluene	0.0049	6.68E − 03	3.40E + 02	2.73	4.4	4.63	535	48.7
19	1,1,2-Trichloroethane		7.40E − 04	4.30E + 01	2.47	nonflam	4.6	4500	
20	1,1,1-Trichloroethane		1.72E − 02	4.00E + 02	2.5	nonflam	4.53	1500	
21	Trichloroethylene		9.10E − 03	5.50E + 02	2.29	nonflam	2.15	1100	
22	Vinyl chloride	0.19000	8.60E − 02	3.55E + 05	1.38	−78.9	3.66	2670	2760.3
23	o-Xylene		5.27E − 03		2.77	17.1	3.66	175	
24	m-Xylene		5.20E − 03		3.2	29.4	3.66	130	
25	p-Xylene		5.27E − 03		3.15	27.2	3.66	198	

(Continued)

No.	Compound	Molecular Weight	Boiling Point (°C)	Vapor Pressure (mm Hg)	Diffusivity in Water (cm²/sec) ×10E − 05	Liquid Density (g/cm³)	Odor Threshold (ppm)	Diffusivity in Air (cm²/sec)
1	Acetone	58.08	56.2	266	1.1400	0.790	100	0.1240
2	Acrylonitrile	53.06	77.4	114	1.3400	0.810	21.4	0.1220
3	Benzene	78.12	80.1	95.2	0.9940	0.879	0.84	0.0932
4	Carbon tetrachloride	153.82	76.7	113	0.8840	1.595	21.4	0.0632
5	Chlorobenzene	112.56	131.6	11.8	0.9000	1.170	0.21	0.0730
6	Chloroform	119.38	61.2	208	1.0600	1.489	675	0.0888
7	Dichlorobenzene, o-	147.00	179.0	1.5	0.7900	1.310	2–4	0.0690
	Dichlorobenzene, m-	147.00	172.0	2.28	0.7860	1.290	0.02	0.0692
	Dichlorobenzene, p-	147.00	173.4	1.2	0.7900	1.290	15–30	0.0690
8	1,1-Dichloroethane	98.96	57.0	234	0.9880	1.256	120	0.0919
9	1,2-Dichloroethane	98.96	83.5	80	0.9880	1.256	3–100	0.0907
10	Ethylbenzene	106.16	136.2	10	0.7800	0.870	0.46–0.60	0.0750
11	Isopropyl alcohol	60.09	82.4	42.8	1.0400	0.790	7.5	0.0980
12	Methylene chloride	84.93	40.1	400	1.6600	1.327	25–307	0.1000
13	Methyl ethyl ketone	72.11	79.6	100	0.9800	0.820	2	0.0808
14	Methyl t-butyl ether	88.15	55.0	245	0.8026	0.758		0.0806
15	Napthalene	128.19	218.0	0.023	0.7500	1.140	0.003	0.0590
16	Phenol	94.10	182.0	0.0341	0.9000	1.070	0.016	
17	Tetrachloroethylene	165.83	121.0	19	0.8200	1.624	50	0.0720
18	Toluene	92.14	110.7	30	0.8600	0.840	0.17	0.0870
19	1,1,2-Trichloroethane	133.41	113.7	25	0.8800	1.320		0.0792
20	1,1,1-Trichloroethane	133.41	75.0	123	0.8800	1.330	100	0.0780
21	Trichloroethylene	131.40	86.7	75	0.9100	1.400	21.4	0.0790
22	Vinyl chloride	62.50	−13.9	2660	1.0400	0.908	260	0.0900
23	o-Xylene	106.20	144.0	7	1.0000	0.880	0.17	0.0870
24	m-Xylene	106.20	138.8	8	0.7800	0.860	~1	0.0870
25	p-Xylene	106.20	138.5	9.5	0.7800	0.860	~0.3	0.0700

Appendix B

Chemical and Physical Properties of Selected Organic Compounds (Ambient Pressure and 30°C)

Compound	Formula	MW (gmol)	p (mm Hg)	D (cm²/sec)	H (atm-m³/gmol)	K_{OC} (g/cm³)
Methanol	CH_4O	32	157.095	.16686	1.1E − 6	
Isopropanol	C_3H_8O	60	55.332	.13526		
Ethanol	C_2H_6O	46	71.616	.12730		
Phenol	C_6H_6O	84	.877	.08924		31
Acetone	C_3H_6O	50	249.146	.10930	1.3E − 6	
Methylethyl ketone	C_4H_8O	72	121.791	.09485	6.8E − 6	3.9
Methyl acetate	$C_3H_6O_2$	74	231.980	.10203	2.1E − 5	
Ethyl acetate	$C_4H_8O_2$	88	104.292	.09005	4.3E − 5	
Acetaldehyde	C_2H_4O	44	***	.13249	1.7E − 4	
Acetic acid	$C_2H_4O_2$	60	20.922	.12007		
Cyclohexane	C_6H_{12}	84	721.016	.08045	2.4E − 1	48C
Hexane	C_6H_{14}	86	165.905	.07912	2.2E − 1	400
Styrene	C_8H_8	104	9.505	.07460	3.7E − 3	170
Toluene	C_7H_8	92	37.621	.08301	5.2E − 3	140
o-Xylene	C_8H_{10}	106	10.684	.07597	7.0E − 3	240
Benzene	C_6H_6	78	7.378	.09234	5.5E − 3	83
Pentane	C_5H_{12}	72	544.926	.06737		
Heptane	C_7H_{16}	100	66.549	.07287	1.5E − 0	
Fluorotoluene	C_7H_7F	110	27.098	.07056		
Methyl chloride	CH_2Cl_2	85	531.654	.10830	3.3E − 3	21
Chloroform	$CHCl_3$	120	213.392	.09404	3.4E − 3	36
Carbon tet	CCl_4	154	122.571	.08451	2.0E − 2	130

Compound	Formula					
Tri-Cl-ethane	$C_2H_3Cl_3$	133	151.640	.08447		
(1,1,1)					4.0E − 3	180
(1,1,2)					7.4E − 4	
Dimethylamine	C_2H_7N	45	***	.12577	5.9E − 8	
Ethylamine	C_2H_7H	45	***	.12577		
Aniline	C_6H_7N	93	1.181	.08065	4.3E − 6	14
Tri-Cl-ethylene	C_2HCl_3	131	91.950	.08606	1.4E + 1	5800
Chloromethane	CH_3Cl	51	***	.11627	0.4E	
Bromoethane	CH_3Br	95	1.627	.10830	2.2E − 4	115
Vinyl chloride	C_2H_3Cl	63	***	.11375	2.0E + 2	3800
Chloroethane	C_2H_5Cl	65	***	.11031	1.4E − 2	33
Tri-Cl-F-methane	CCl_3F	138	858.389	.08329	1.2E − 1	127
Dichloroethylene	$C_2H_2Cl_2$	97	774.919	.08386	3.2E − 2	125
Dichloroethane	$C_2H_4Cl_2$	99		.09643		
(1,1)			270		4.7E − 3	43
(1,2)			105		1.6E − 3	33
Dichloropropane (1,2)	$C_3H_6Cl_2$	113	64.214	.08473	2.7E − 3	69
Bromoform	$CHBr_3$	118	8.007	.10860	3.9E − 4	64
Tet-Cl-ethylene	C_2Cl_4	166	23.237	.07852	3.3E − 2	427
Tet-Cl-ethane (1,1,2,2)	$C_2H_2Cl_4$	168	17.283	.07729	6.4E − 4	82
Chlorobenzene	C_6H_5Cl	113	16.671	.07627	4.6E − 3	150
Ethylbenzene	C_8H_{10}	106	12.755	.07070	1.1E − 2	280

*** Means the vapor pressure is greater than 1,000 mm Hg.

Appendix C

Soil-Adsorption Coefficients of Selected Compounds

Chemical	K_{OW}	K_{OC}
Volatiles		
Methyl chloride	8.1	7.5
Methylene chloride	18	16
Chloroform	93	74
Carbon tetrachloride	440	320
Chloroethane	35	30
1,1-Dichloroethane	62	51
1,2-Dichloroethane	30	26
1,1,1-Trichloroethane	150	120
1,1,2-Trichloroethane	150	120
1,1,2,1-Tetrachlorethane	360	260
Hexachloroethane	2,200	1,500
Vinyl chloride	4.0	3.9
1,1 Dichloroethene	30	26
1,2 trans-Dichloroethene	30	26
Trichloroethene	200	150
Tetrachloroethene	760	530
1,2-Dichloropropane	190	140
1,3-Dichloropropene	95	76
Hexachlorobutadiene	5,500	3,400
Hexachlorocyclopentadiene	9,800	5,900
Bromomethane	13	12
Bromodichloromethane	76	61
Dibromochloromethane	120	94
Tribromochloromethane	200	150
Dichlorodifluoromethane	140	110
Trichlorofluoromethane	340	250

(Continued)

Chemical	K_{OW}	K_{OC}
Pesticides		
Acrolein	0.8	0.8
Aldrin	NA	—
Chlordane	560	400
DDD (p,p')	1,000,000	46,000
DDE (p,p')	500,000	24,000
DDT (p,p')	200,000	100,000
Dieldrin	NA	—
Endosulfan (α)	3,500	2,200
Endosulfan sulfate	4,600	2,900
Endrin	400,000	190,000
Heptachlor epoxide	NA	—
Hexachlorocyclohexane (α)	6,500	4,000
Hexachlorocyclohexane (β)	6,300	3,900
Hexachlorocyclohexane (δ)	14,000	8,300
Hexachlorocyclohexane (γ)	5,200	3,300
TCDD	NA	—
Isophorone	50	41
Toxaphene	2,000	1,300
PCBs		
Aroclor 1016	24,000	14,000
Aroclor 1221	12,000	7,200
Aroclor 1232	35,000	20,000
Aroclor 1242	380,000	180,000
Aroclor 1248	1,300,000	580,000
Aroclor 1254	1,070,000	490,000
Aroclor 1260	14,000,000	5,500,000

NA—Data not available.
K_{OW}—Octanol/water partition coefficient.
K_{OC}—Soil adsorption constant referenced to organic content.

Appendix D

Chemical and Physical Properties of the Waste Material Affecting Emissions

Property	Effect
Saturation concentration	The waste will tend to reach equilibrium with the soil vapor. If sufficient waste is present, the equilibrium concentration within the air-filled voids of the soil matrix will reach saturation. Because the rate of emission to the atmosphere is directly proportional to the soil vapor concentration, the emission rate will increase as saturation concentration increases.
Diffusion coefficient	Compounds with high overall diffusion coefficients will be emitted at higher rates than those with lower diffusion coefficients via increased transport, on a relative basis. The overall diffusion coefficient may be comprised of diffusion through the soil–water interface, soil–air interface, soil, water, air, and soil vapor.
Molecular weight	Lower molecular weight compounds typically have higher volatilization and diffusion coefficients. Other compound characteristics may predominate. Molecular weight is used to determine diffusion rates in some predictive models.
Partial pressure of constituents	High partial pressure increases the emission rate of a species by increasing its soil vapor concentration.
Weight fraction	An effect similar to partial pressure, it is used as an input to some predictive models. It is not as important as Henry's law constant.
Combination of constituents	This increases the complexity of the emissions process and determines the emission rate. It may change over time as more volatile species are lost.
Concentration of waste	Increasing waste concentration increases the emission rate for dilute wastes by increasing the vapor pressure and, therefore, the vapor concentration.

(Continued)

Property	Effect
Henry's law constant	This is used to determine diffusion coefficients. A high Henry's law constant produces a high diffusion rate.
Porosity	This is one of the controlling factors for diffusion through the soil. Emission rates typically increase with increasing soil porosity. Total porosity, i.e., dry soil, may represent worst-case conditions for predictive models. Air-filled porosity may be a more realistic parameter for many sites.
Adsorption/absorption properties of soil	Soil with high sorption properties will reduce the vapor density of the sorbed compounds and, therefore, the emission rate. The effect may be minimal where high waste concentrations saturate the sorption sites. The effect may be reversed, causing increased emissions.
Soil moisture	Its effect varies. High moisture will reduce the air-filled porosity, with pores being filled under worst-case conditions, and, therefore, should reduce the emission rate. Moisture may be preferentially adsorbed by the soil, releasing volatiles and increasing the emission rate. Drying of soil may increase available sorption sites. Moisture is required for the wick effect.
Wick effect	Soil moisture may draw waste constituents to the surface through the soil pores. This process can increase the concentration of the constituents at the surface and, therefore, increase the emission rate.
Particle size distribution	This affects the total soil porosity and soil pore continuity. Increased soil pore continuity increases the emission rate. A higher percent of fines typically will increase particulate emissions.
Organic content of soil	High organic content will increase the sorptive characteristics of the soil and reduce the emission rate. High organic content also will increase microbial action.
Microbial activity	Its effect varies. It may reduce the emission rate by biological reduction of the waste present. It also may increase the emission rate because of gas formation, which carries volatile species to the surface.
Depth of landfill cover	Emission rates decrease with increasing depth (thickness) of cover as the diffusion path increases. For an open dump or landfill, the cover thickness is zero.
Compaction of landfill cover	Increasing compaction reduces the soil porosity and disrupts continuity of the soil pores, thereby reducing the emission rate.
Ground cover	Soil cover, typically vegetation, will reduce particulate emissions by reducing the erodibility of the soil. It also will help hold soil moisture, which reduces the air-filled porosity and reduces volatile emissions.

(*Continued*)

Property	Effect
Size of landfill/lagoon	The emission rate is directly proportional to the size of the landfill or lagoon.
Amount of exposed waste	Emission will increase when waste is exposed at the surface, because of both volatilization and wind erosion.
Water depth in lagoon	Water overlying waste will act as a cover. Diffusion through water may control the emission rate.
Aeration of lagoons	Aeration increases the emission of volatile and particulates with increasing volume of air used and/or agitation. The effect is due to air stripping of volatiles and bulk transport of liquid particles.
Temperature	Increasing temperature increases the volatilization rate for organic species and, therefore, the emission rate. Increasing temperature reduces soil moisture, increasing air-filled porosity and the emission rate.
Wind	Wind removes the volatilized compound concentration in the boundary layer over the site, maintaining the driving force for volatilization. Increasing wind speed reduces the boundary layer over the site. Wind causes turbulence within the boundary layer, providing the driving force for surface soil/waste erosion and increasing the particulate emission rate.
Cloud cover	Increased cloud cover reduces solar heating of the surface and, therefore, the volatilization rate from the surface. It also affects wind stability.
Precipitation	Emissions are reduced by reducing the air-filled soil porosity. Precipitation may increase landfill emission by displacing soil vapor from soil voids. It may increase surface water and air emissions by floating waste constituents to the surface. Precipitation increases agitation of the lagoon surface, potentially increasing emissions, but it also increases the water depth over waste in the lagoon.
Humidity	Increasing the partial pressure of water vapor in air reduces the capacity for some types of volatilized material. It may reduce the air-filled soil porosity.
Barometric pressure	Changing barometric pressures cause bulk flow of soil vapor into/out of soil. The overall net effect is to increase the emission rate. The effect increases with the frequency and the scale of barometric changes.

Appendix E

Calculated Diffusivities of Some Selected Compounds in Water at 25°C

Compound	Diffusivity (cm^2/sec)
Acrolein	1.2×10^{-5}
Acrylonitrile	1.23×10^{-5}
Benzene	1.02×10^{-5}
Benzidine	
Carbon tetrachloride (tetrachloromethane)	9.7×10^{-6}
Chlorobenzene	9.43×10^{-6}
1,2,4-Trichlorobenzene	8.34×10^{-6}
Hexachlorobenzene	7.8×10^{-6}
1,2-Dichlorobenzene	1.1×10^{-5}
1,1,1-Trichloroethane	9.5×10^{-6}
Hexachloroethane	8.84×10^{-6}
1,1-Dichloroethane	1.06×10^{-5}
1,1,2-Trichloroethane	9.97×10^{-6}
1,1,2,2-Tetrachloroethane	9.25×10^{-6}
Chloroethane	1.18×10^{-5}
Bis(chloromethyl) ether	1.04×10^{-5}
Bis(2-chloroethyl) ether	7.68×10^{-6}
2-Chloroethyl vinyl ether (mixed)	8.64×10^{-6}
2-Chloronaphthalene	8.2×10^{-6}
2,4,6-Trichlorophenol	8.04×10^{-6}
Parachlorometacresol	7.67×10^{-6}
Chloroform (trichloromethane)	1.09×10^{-5}
2-Chlorophenol	9.32×10^{-6}
1,2-Dichlorobenzene	8.87×10^{-6}
1,3-Dichlorobenzene	8.8×10^{-6}
1,4-Dichlorobenzene	9.48×10^{-6}
1,1-Dichloroethylene	1.09×10^{-5}
1,2-*trans*-Dichloroethylene	1.11×10^{-5}

(*Continued*)

Compound	Diffusivity (cm²/sec)
2,4-Dichlorophenol	8.63×10^{-6}
1,2-Dichloropropane	9.66×10^{-6}
1,3-Dichloropropylene (1,3-dichloropropene)	1.01×10^{-5}
2,4-Dimethylphenol	8.27×10^{-6}
2,4-Dinitrotoluene	7.86×10^{-6}
2,6-Dinitrotoluene	7.86×10^{-6}
1,2-Diphenylhydrazine	
Ethylbenzene	8.87×10^{-6}
Fluoranthene	7.14×10^{-6}
Bis(2-chloroisopropyl) ether	6.53×10^{-6}
Methylene chloride (dichloromethane)	1.25×10^{-5}
Methyl chloride (chloromethane)	1.39×10^{-5}
Methyl bromide (bromomethane)	1.37×10^{-5}
Bromoform (tribromomethane)	1.03×10^{-5}
Dichlorobromomethane	1.07×10^{-5}
Trichlorofluoromethane	9.35×10^{-6}
Dichlorodifluoromethane	$9.4 \ \times 10^{-6}$
Chlorodibromomethane	1.05×10^{-5}
Hexachlorobutadiene	7.32×10^{-6}
Hexachlorocyclopentadiene	6.44×10^{-6}
Isophorone	7.48×10^{-6}
Naphthalene	8.89×10^{-6}
Nitrobenzene	$7.8 \ \times 10^{-6}$
2-Nitrophenol	9.12×10^{-6}
N-nitrosodi-*n*-propylamine	7.72×10^{-6}
Pentachlorophenol	7.97×10^{-6}
Phenol	1.03×10^{-5}
Acenaphthylene	6.94×10^{-6}
Anthracene	$7.7 \ \times 10^{-6}$
Fluorene	8.27×10^{-6}
Phenanthrene	7.44×10^{-6}
Tetrachloroethylene	9.41×10^{-6}
Toluene	8.23×10^{-6}
Trichloroethylene	1.02×10^{-5}
Vinyl chloride (chloroethylene)	1.19×10^{-5}
PCB-1242 (Aroclor 1242)	7.08×10^{-6}
PCB-1254 (Aroclor 1254)	none
PCB-1221 (Aroclor 1221)	none
PCB-1232 (Aroclor 1232)	none
PCB-1245 (Aroclor 1245)	none
PCB-1260 (Aroclor 1260)	none
PCB-1016 (Aroclor 1016)	none

Appendix F

Henry's Law Constants of Some RCRA Waste Constituents

Waste Name	Henry's Constant (Hwang, 1982; Versar, 1984) (atm-m^3/mol)	Vapor Pressure (Hwang, 1982) (mm Hg)
Values of H above 10^{-3}		
Bis(2-ethyl hexyl phthalate)	26.6	
Cyanogen	9.91	
Reserpine	4.28	
Dichlorodifluoromethane	2.75	
Chloromethane	0.38	376.5
Chloroethene	0.199	
Phosphine	0.19	
Cyclohexane	0.18	
2-Nitropropane	0.12	
Bromomethane	0.106	
Trichloromonofluoromethane	5.8×10^{-2}	1,657
2,3,4,6-Tetrachlorophenol	4.5×10^{-2}	
1,3-Pentadiene	4.2×10^{-2}	
Pentachloronitrobenzene	2.9×10^{-2}	
Tetrachloroethylene	2.87×10^{-2}	19.6
Hexachloropropene	2.5×10^{-2}	
Tetrachloromethane	3.02×10^{-2}	
Hexachlorocyclopentadiene	1.64×10^{-2}	0.081
1,1-Dichloroethylene	1.50×10^{-2}	591
Cumene	1.40×10^{-2}	
DDD	1.26×10^{-2}	
Carbon disulfide	1.2×10^{-2}	
Trichloroethylene	1.17×10^{-2}	74
Mercury	1.14×10^{-2}	

(*Continued*)

Waste Name	Henry's Constant (Hwang, 1982; Versar, 1984) (atm-m^3/mol)	Vapor Pressure (Hwang, 1982) (mm Hg)
Hexachlorobutadiene	1.03×10^{-3}	0.15
Hexachloroethane	9.85×10^{-3}	
Hexachlorobutadiene	9.14×10^{-3}	
Aroclor 1254	8.37×10^{-3}	
3-Methylcholanthrene	$7.7 \ \times 10^{-3}$	
Formaldehyde		3.286 (U.S. EPA, 1980a)
1,2-Dichloroethylene (CIS)	$6.6 \ \times 10^{-3}$	
Toluene	5.93×10^{-3}	28.4
Ethylbenzene	6.44×10^{-3}	9.5
Furan	$5.7 \ \times 10^{-3}$	
Benzene	5.55×10^{-3}	95
1,1-Dichloroethane	5.45×10^{-3}	234
1,2-Dichloroethylene (trans)	5.32×10^{-3}	200
o-xylene	5.27×10^{-3}	
Methyl iodide	$5.0 \ \times 10^{-3}$	
1,1,1-Trichloroethane	4.92×10^{-3}	
Toxaphene	4.89×10^{-3}	
1,3-Dichloropropane	$4.2 \ \times 10^{-3}$	
Methanethiol	$4.0 \ \times 10^{-3}$	
Chlorobenzene	3.93×10^{-3}	12
1,3-Dichloropropylene	3.55×10^{-3}	25
Chloroform	3.39×10^{-3}	200
Cyanogen chloride	$3.2 \ \times 10^{-3}$	
Methylene chloride	3.19×10^{-3}	455
1,2-Dichloropropane	$2.8 \ \times 10^{-3}$	50
1,1,1,2-Tetrachloroethane	2.76×10^{-3}	
4-Bromopropylphenylether	2.74×10^{-3}	
p-Dichlorobenzene	2.72×10^{-3}	
m-Dichlorobenzene	2.63×10^{-3}	2
m-Xylene	2.55×10^{-3}	
p-Xylene	2.51×10^{-3}	
Hexachlorohexahydro-exo,exo-dimethanonaphthalene	2.49×10^{-3}	
p-Dichlorobenzene	2.37×10^{-3}	
Pentachloroethane	2.17×10^{-3}	
Bromodichloromethane	2.12×10^{-3}	
Octachlorocamphene	2.01×10^{-3}	
Dichlorobenzene	1.94×10^{-3}	1.5
Dimethylcarbamoylchloride	$1.8 \ \times 10^{-3}$	
Hexachlorobenzene	$1.7 \ \times 10^{-3}$	
Heptachlor	1.48×10^{-3}	3.7×10^{-7} (Freeman and Schroy, 1984)
1,2,4-Trichlorobenzene	1.42×10^{-3}	0.3

(*Continued*)

Waste Name	Henry's Constant (Hwang, 1982; Versar, 1984) (atm-m^3/mol)	Vapor Pressure (Hwang, 1982) (mm Hg)
Pentachlorobenzene	1.3×10^{-3}	
1,1,2-Trichloroethane	1.18×10^{-3}	
1,2-Dichloroethane	1.10×10^{-3}	86
Values of H below 10^{-3} to 10^{-5}		
Ethyl ether	8.69×10^{-4}	
2-Cyclohexyl,4,6-dinitrophenol	8.37×10^{-4}	
N-Nitroso-di-*n*-butylamine	7.9×10^{-4}	
Dibromochloromethane	7.83×10^{-4}	50
2,6-Dinitrotoluene	7.42×10^{-4}	
2-Chloroethyl vinyl ether	7.35×10^{-4}	
Ethylene dibromide	6.25×10^{-4}	
Bromoform	5.32×10^{-4}	5.6
Aldrin	4.96×10^{-4}	6×10^{-6} (Freeman and Schroy, 1984)
Naphthalene	4.8×10^{-4}	
1,1,2,2-Tetrachloroethane	4.7×10^{-4}	
N-Nitroso-N-methyl urethane	4.17×10^{-4}	
Dipropylamine	3.32×10^{-4}	
Methylene bromide	3.16×10^{-4}	
B-Chloronapthalene	3.15×10^{-4}	
Methyl methacrylate	3.11×10^{-4}	
Benzenethiol	3.10×10^{-4}	
Formaldehyde	2.92×10^{-4}	
Ethyl acrylate	2.71×10^{-4}	
Bischloromethylether	2.50×10^{-4}	
Benzylchloride	2.36×10^{-4}	
Dihydrosafrole	2.30×10^{-4}	
Diallate	1.99×10^{-4}	
Dinoseb	1.82×10^{-4}	
Benzal chloride	1.70×10^{-4}	
5-Nitro-*o*-toluidine	1.67×10^{-4}	
1,2-Dibromo-3-chloropropane	1.59×10^{-4}	
Ethyl methacrylate	1.49×10^{-4}	
Tris(2,3-dibromopropyl)phosphate	1.46×10^{-4}	
4-Methyl-2-pentanone	1.32×10^{-4}	
Ethyl acrylate	1.20×10^{-4}	
Fluorene	1.17×10^{-4}	
Acenaphthylene	1.14×10^{-4}	
Benzotrichloride	1.12×10^{-4}	
Tetrahydrofuran	1.08×10^{-4}	
Trichloromethylmercaptan	1.04×10^{-4}	

(Continued)

Waste Name	Henry's Constant (Hwang, 1982; Versar, 1984) (atm-m^3/mol)	Vapor Pressure (Hwang, 1982) (mm Hg)
Bis-2-chloroisopropyl ether	1.03×10^{-4}	
1,1,2,2-Tetrachloroethane	4.7×10^{-4}	
1,2,4,5-Tetrachlorobenzene	1.0×10^{-4}	
N-Nitrosopiperidine	9.78×10^{-5}	
Acrylonitrile	9.2×10^{-5}	
Methapyriline	7.6×10^{-5}	
Acrolein	6.79×10^{-5}	
1,4-Dichloro-2-butene	6.78×10^{-5}	
Trichloroacetaldehyde	6.77×10^{-4}	
Osmium tetroxide	5.86×10^{-5}	
Dieldrin	5.8×10^{-5}	
N-Nitrosomethylvinylamine	5.65×10^{-5}	
Kepone	5.6×10^{-5}	
DDT	5.2×10^{-5}	1.9×10^{-5} (Freeman and Schroy, 1984)
Nitroglycerin	5.18×10^{-5}	
Chlordane	4.8×10^{-5}	
Diethylphthalate	4.75×10^{-5}	
α,α-Dimethylphenethylamine	3.9×10^{-5}	
1-Chloro-2,3-epoxypropane	3.8×10^{-5}	
Paraldehyde	3.66×10^{-5}	
Ethylene oxide	3.63×10^{-5}	
Heptachlor epoxide	3.2×10^{-5}	2×10^{-5} (30°C) (Freeman and Schroy, 1984)
Dichloroethylether	2.58×10^{-5}	
Cyclohexanone	2.56×10^{-5}	
Endosulfan	2.5×10^{-5}	
Propanenitrile	2.4×10^{-5}	
2-Butanone	2.4×10^{-5}	
2-Picoline	2.4×10^{-5}	
1,1,2,2-Tetrachloroethane	4.7×10^{-4}	
Nitrobenzene	2.4×10^{-5}	
Methyl aziridine	2.22×10^{-5}	
2,6-Dichlorophenol	2.0×10^{-5}	
Acetophenone	1.41×10^{-5}	
2,4-Dimethylphenol	1.18×10^{-5}	
Crotonaldehyde	1.13×10^{-5}	
N-Nitrosopyrrolidine	1.13×10^{-5}	
Dieldrin	1.1×10^{-5}	
Safrole	1.08×10^{-5}	
Isobutanol	1.03×10^{-5}	
4-Chloro-*o*-toluidine	1.02×10^{-5}	

(Continued)

Waste Name	Henry's Constant (Hwang, 1982; Versar, 1984) (atm-m³/mol)	Vapor Pressure (Hwang, 1982) (mm Hg)
Values of H from 10^{-5} to 10^{-7}		
Chloromethyl methylether	9.12×10^{-6}	
Diisopropylfluorophosphate	9.1×10^{-6}	
Pronamide	9.0×10^{-6}	
∞-Diethyl-*o*-pyrazinyl-phosphoro-thioate	8.58×10^{-6}	
α-Toluidine hydrochloride	7.55×10^{-6}	
Ammonium Picrate	7.4×10^{-6}	
Di-*n*-propylnitrosamine	7.2×10^{-6}	
n-Butanol	7.0×10^{-6}	
Acetone	6.8×10^{-6}	
Tetranitromethane	6.33×10^{-6}	
2,4,5-Trichlorophenol	6.0×10^{-6}	
2,4-Dichlorophenol	5.62×10^{-6}	
Phorate	5.47×10^{-6}	
N-Nitroso-N-ethylurea	5.4×10^{-6}	
2-Naphthalamine	5.4×10^{-6}	
2,4,6-Trichlorophenol	4.82×10^{-6}	
Chloroacetaldehyde	4.7×10^{-6}	
o-Chlorophenol	4.7×10^{-6}	
4-Pyridinamine	4.4×10^{-6}	
Endrin	4.2×10^{-6}	
1-Naphthalamine	4.1×10^{-6}	
Isosafrole	4.08×10^{-6}	
Furfural	3.6×10^{-6}	
1,4-Naphthalenedione	3.6×10^{-6}	
3-chloropropionitrile	3.5×10^{-6}	
Allyl alcohol	3.47×10^{-6}	
Dimethyl sulfate	3.37×10^{-6}	
Aniline	3.07×10^{-6}	
p-Chloroaniline	3.0×10^{-6}	
Disulfoton	2.59×10^{-6}	
Acetonitrile	2.47×10^{-6}	
N-Nitroso-N-methylurea	2.20×10^{-6}	
Cresols	2.0×10^{-6}	
Phenacetin	1.4×10^{-6}	
4,6-Dinitro-*o*-cresol	1.4×10^{-6}	
Phenol	1.3×10^{-6}	
Parathion	1.21×10^{-6}	
Methanol	1.1×10^{-6}	
Dibutylphthalate	1.09×10^{-6}	
p-Nitroaniline	1.0×10^{-6}	

(*Continued*)

Waste Name	Henry's Constant (Hwang, 1982; Versar, 1984) (atm-m^3/mol)	Vapor Pressure (Hwang, 1982) (mm Hg)
1,4-Diethylenedioxide	7.14×10^{-7}	
1,4-Dioxane	7.0×10^{-7}	
N-Nitrosodiethylamine	6.0×10^{-7}	
Ethyl-4,4'-dichlorobenzilate	5.89×10^{-7}	
Glycidylaldeyde	5.80×10^{-7}	
p-Benzoquinone	5.0×10^{-7}	
Lindane	4.93×10^{-7}	
Pentachlorophenol	4.8×10^{-7}	
Hydrocyanic acid	4.65×10^{-7}	
Formic acid	4.4×10^{-7}	
α-Hexachlorocyclohexane	3.16×10^{-7}	
Di-n-octylphthalate	3.0×10^{-7}	
4-Chloro-m-cresol	2.83×10^{-7}	
Bis-2-chloromethoxymethane	2.77×10^{-7}	
Methyl parathion	1.97×10^{-7}	
Saccharin	1.90×10^{-7}	
Methylthiouracil	1.80×10^{-7}	
Nicotine	1.6×10^{-7}	
N-Phenylthiourea	1.47×10^{-7}	
4,4'-Methylenebis (2-chloroaniline)	1.40×10^{-7}	
Bromoacetone	1.17×10^{-7}	
Malononitrile	1.0×10^{-7}	
2,4-Dinitrotoluene	7.6×10^{-8}	
2,4-D	7.5×10^{-8}	
Dimethylamine	5.9×10^{-8}	
2,4,5-T	3.44×10^{-8}	
Ethylmethanesulfonate	3.14×10^{-8}	
Dimethylnitrosamine	3.0×10^{-8}	
Chlornaphazine	2.8×10^{-8}	
1-(α-Chlorophenylthiourea)	2.51×10^{-8}	
Ethyl carbamate	2.0×10^{-8}	
1,2,7,8-Dibenzopyrene	2.0×10^{-8}	
2-Propyn-1-ol	2.0×10^{-8}	
Benzidine	1.91×10^{-8}	
Silvex	1.80×10^{-8}	
Acrylamide	1.49×10^{-8}	
1,2,3,4-Diepoxybutene	1.02×10^{-8}	
n-Nitrosodiethanolamine	8.0×10^{-9}	
3,4-Benzacridine	7.0×10^{-9}	
Pyridine	7.0×10^{-9}	
1,2-Benzanthracene	3.4×10^{-9}	
Diethyl-p-nitrophenylphosphate	2.83×10^{-9}	
Fluoroacetamide	2.33×10^{-9}	
Toluenediamine	2.30×10^{-9}	

(Continued)

Waste Name	Henry's Constant (Hwang, 1982; Versar, 1984) (atm-m^3/mol)	Vapor Pressure (Hwang, 1982) (mm Hg)
3,3'-Dimethylbenzidine	1.75×10^{-9}	
Benzo[a]pyrene	1.38×10^{-9}	
7,12-Dimethylbenz[A]anthracene	1.03×10^{-9}	
3,3'-Dichlorobenzidine	1.0×10^{-9}	
Phenylmercuricacetate	1.0×10^{-9}	
Thiofanox	9.37×10^{-10}	
2-Acetylaminofluorene	4.4×10^{-10}	
Mitomycin C	2.5×10^{-10}	
Cyclophosphamide	2.37×10^{-10}	
α-Naphthylthiourea	2.26×10^{-10}	
Urcil, 5[bis-2-chloromethylamino]	1.0×10^{-10}	
Aldicarb	1.0×10^{-10}	
Dibenz[AH]anthracene	1.0×10^{-10}	
Methomyl	1.0×10^{-10}	
Dimethoate	1.0×10^{-10}	
Ethylenebis(dithiocarbamic acid)	1.0×10^{-10}	
2-Methylacetonitrile	1.0×10^{-10}	
4-Nitrophenol	1.0×10^{-10}	
Maleic anhydride	1.0×10^{-10}	
Phthalic anhydride	1.0×10^{-10}	
Diethylstilbestrol	5.1×10^{-11}	
2,4-D salts and esters	3.6×10^{-11}	
3,3'-Dimethoxybenzidine	1.0×10^{-11}	
1,3-Propane sultone	1.0×10^{-11}	
1,2-Diphenylhydrazine	1.0×10^{-11}	
Streptozotocin	1.0×10^{-11}	
Melphalan	1.0×10^{-11}	
Chlorambucil	2.1×10^{-12}	
Chrysene	1.0×10^{-12}	
5-(Aminomethyl)-3-isoxazolol	1.0×10^{-13}	
Resorcinol	1.0×10^{-13}	
Strychnine	1.0×10^{-14}	
Warfarin	1.0×10^{-15}	
Brucine	1.0×10^{-18}	
Hexachlorophene	1.0×10^{-18}	
Daunomycin	2.2×10^{-19}	

Wastes with No Henry's
Constant Value Available

Chromium
Arsenic
Lead

(*Continued*)

Waste Name	Henry's Constant (Hwang, 1982; Versar, 1984) (atm-m³/mol)	Vapor Pressure (Hwang, 1982) (mm Hg)
Cadmium		
Barium		
Acetaldehyde		
Selenium		
Silver		
Arsenic acid		
Benzene, 1,3-Trinitro-Sodium cyanide		
Ethylenimine		
2,4-Dinitrophenol		
Benzenesulfonyl chloride		
2,4,STP Silvex		
Hydrofluoric acid		
Lindane		
Aluminum phosphide		
Copper cyanide		
2,3,7,8-TCDD		1.45×10^{-9} (Thibodeaux and Lipsky, 1985)

Appendix G

Major Features of the ISC Model

Polar or Cartesian coordinate systems.

Rural or one of three urban options.

Plume rise due to momentum and buoyancy as a function of downwind distance for stack emissions (Briggs, 1969, 1971, 1972, 1973, and 1975).

Building wake effects using methods of Huber and Snyder (Huber and Snyder, 1976, 1982; Huber, 1977) or Schulman and Scire (Schulman and Hanna, 1986; Schulman and Scire, 1986) depending on the stack height to building height ratio (see Section 2.4.1.1.d), for evaluating building wake effects. The Schulman and Scire approach uses building dimensions as functions of direction.

Procedures suggested by Briggs (1974) for evaluating stack-tip downwash.

Separation of multiple point sources.

Consideration of the effects of gravitational settling and dry deposition on ambient particulate concentrations.

Capability of simulating point, line, volume, and area sources.

Capability to calculate dry deposition.

Variation with height of wind speed (wind-profile exponent law).

Concentration estimates for 1-hour to annual average.

Terrain-adjustment procedures for elevated terrain including a terrain truncation algorithm.

(Continued)

Consideration of time-dependent exponential decay of pollutants.

The method of Pasquill (1976) to account for buoyancy-induced dispersion.

A regulatory default option to set various model options and parameters to EPA recommended values.

Procedure for calm-wind processing.

Capability to treat height of receptor above ground ("flagpole" receptors).

System Description

The ISC Short-Term (ISCST) Model Program

Figure G-1 is a schematic diagram of the ISC Model short-term computer program (ISCST). As shown by the figure, ISCST directly accepts the preprocessed meteorological data tape produced by the RAMMET preprocessor. This meteorological preprocessor program is described in the User's Manual for Single-Source (CRSTER) Model (EPA, 1977), as updated by Catalano (1986). Alternatively, hourly meteorological data may be input by card deck. Program control parameters, source data, and receptor data are input by card deck. The program produces printouts of calculated concentration or deposition values.

The ISC Long-Term (ISCLT) Model Program

Figure G-2 is a schematic diagram of the ISC Model long-term computer program (ISCLT). As shown by the figure, program control parameters, meterological data, source data, and receptor data are input by card deck. The program produces printouts of calculated concentration or deposition values. Additionally, all input data and the results of all calculations may be stored on an optimal master tape inventory which can be used as input to update future runs. The master tape file stores the concentration or deposition calculated for each source at each receptor. Sources may be added, deleted, or altered in update runs using card input for the affected sources. Concentration or deposition calculations are then made for those sources only, and the concentration or deposition values calculated for each source are resummed to obtain an updated estimate of the concentration or deposition produced at each receptor by all sources.

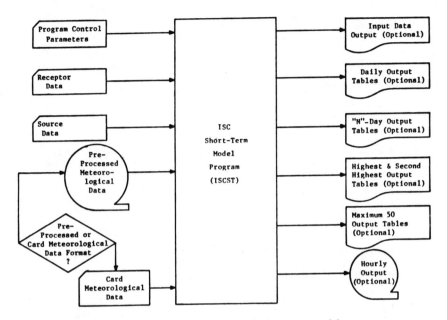

Figure G-1.   Schematic diagram of ISC short-term model program.

Summary of Input Data
The ISC Short-Term (ISCST) Model Program

The input requirements for the ISC Model short-term computer program (ISCST) consist of four categories:

- Meteorological data
- Source data
- Receptor data
- Program control parameters

a. *Meteorological Data.* Meteorological inputs required by the ISCST program include hourly estimates of the wind direction, wind speed, ambient air temperature, Pasquill stability category, mixing height, wind-profile exponent, and vertical potential temperature gradient. The magnetic tape output of the meteorological data preprocessor program and the program default values for the wind-profile exponent and the vertical potential temperature gradient satisfy all ISCST hourly meteorological data requirements. Alternatively, hourly meteorological data can be input by means of a card deck. When this is done, the use of the calm process-

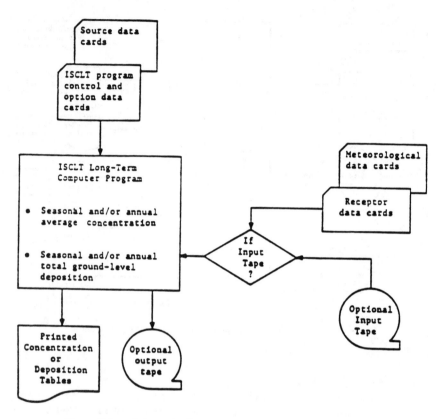

Figure G-2.   Schematic diagram of ISC long-term model program.

ing feature (described in Section 1.5.1.d) is not permitted. The number of hours for which concentration or deposition calculations can be made ranges from 1 to 8,784 (i.e., up to every hour of a 366-day year).

b. *Source Data.* The ISCST program accepts three source types: stack, area, and volume. For each source, input data requirements include the source location with respect to a user-specified origin, the source elevation (if terrain effects are to be included in the model calculations), and the pollutant emission rate. For each stack, additional source input requirements include the physical stack height, the stack inner diameter, the stack exit temperature, and the stack exit velocity. If aerodynamic wake effects due to an adjacent building are to be considered, the length, width, and height of the building are required as well. For certain stack heights and building dimensions, 36 direction-specific building heights and widths are input. The horizontal dimensions and effective emission height are required for each area source or volume source. If the calculations are to consider particulates with appreciable gravitational settling velocities, source inputs for each source also include the mass fraction of particulates in each gravitational settling-velocity category as well as the surface reflection coefficient and settling velocity of each settling-velocity category. Because industrial pollutant emission rates are often highly variable, emission rates for each source may be held constant or varied as follows:

- By hour of the day.
- By season or month.
- By hour of the day and season.
- By stability and wind speed (applies to fugitive sources of wind-blown particulates).

c. *Receptor Data.* The ISCST program uses either a polar (r, θ) or a Cartesian (X, Y) coordinate system. The typical polar receptor array consists of 36 radials (one for every 10 degrees of azimuth) and five to ten downwind ring distances for a total of 180 to 360 receptors. However, the user is not restricted to a 10-degree angular separation of receptors. The polar receptor array is always centered at $X = 0$, $Y = 0$. Receptor locations in the Cartesian coordinate system may be given as Universal Transverse Mercator (UTM) coordinates or as X (east–west) and Y (north–south) coordinates with respect to a user-specified origin. Discrete receptor points corresponding to the locations of air quality monitors, elevated terrain, or other points of interest may also be used with either coordinate system. If terrain effects are to be included in the calculations, the ground level elevation of each receptor is required. If receptor heights above ground ("flagpole" receptors) are to be modeled, the receptor height above local terrain is also required. Both terrain elevation and receptor height above local terrain may be input for the same receptor.

d. *Program Control Parameters and Options.* The ISCST program allows the user to select from a number of model options. The available options include:

- Concentration/Deposition Option—Directs the program to calculate average concentration or total deposition.
- Receptor Grid System Option—Selects a Cartesian or a polar receptor grid system.
- Discrete Receptor Option—Allows the user to arbitrarily place receptors at any points using either a Cartesian or a polar coordinate system.

- Receptor Terrain Elevation Option—Allows the user to specify an elevation for each receptor (level terrain is assumed if this option is not exercised).
- Tape/File Output Option—Directs the program to output the results of all concentration or deposition calculations to tape/file.
- Print Input Data Option—Directs the program to print program control parameters, source data, and receptor data; the user may also direct the program to print the hourly meteorological data if this option is exercised. This option prints all input data after all input data has been read.
- Output Tables Option—Specifies which of the five types of output tables are to be printed (see Section 3.1.3).
- Meteorological Data Option—Directs the program to read hourly data from either the meteorological preprocessor format or a card image format. When card image format is selected, the calm processing feature and the regulatory default option are not used.
- Rural/Urban Option—Specifies whether the concentration or deposition calculations are made in the Rural Mode, Urban Mode 1, Urban Mode 2, or Urban Mode 3 (see Section 2.2.1.1).
- Wind-Profile Exponent Option—Directs the program to read user-provided wind-profile exponents or to use the default values.
- Vertical Potential Temperature Gradient Option—Directs the program to read user-provided vertical potential temperature gradients or to use the default values.
- Source Combination Option—Allows the user to specify the combinations of sources for which concentration or deposition estimates are required.
- Single Time Period Interval Option—Directs the program to print concentration or deposition values for a specific time interval within a day (for example, the third 3-hour period).
- Variable Emission Rate Option—Allows the user to specify scalars which are multiplied by the source's average emission rate; the scalars may vary by season or month, by hour of the day, by season and hour of the day, or by wind speed and stability.
- Plume Rise as a Function of Distance Option—Allows the user to direct the program to calculate plume rise as a function of downwind distance or to calculate final plume rise at all downwind distances.
- Stack-Tip Downwash Option—Allows the user to direct the program to use the Briggs (1974) procedures to account for stack-tip downwash for all stack sources.
- Buoyancy-Induced Dispersion Option—Allows the user to direct the program to use the Pasquill (1976) method to parameterize the growth of plumes during the plume rise phase.

- Regulatory Default Option—Allows the user to direct the program to use the following features generally recommended by EPA for regulatory applications:
  1) Tape/file meteorological input assumed.
  2) Final plume rise at all receptor locations.
  3) Stack-tip downwash.
  4) Buoyancy-induced dispersion.
  5) Default wind profile coefficients (urban or rural).
  6) Default vertical potential temperature gradients.
  7) Calm wind processing.
  8) A decay half life of 4 hours for SO_2, urban; otherwise the half life is set to infinity.
  9) Revised wake effects procedures.
  In ISCST all other options remain available to the user, except that if card image meteorological data input is used, the calm processing and regulatory default option features are not used.
- Calm Processing Option—Allows the user to direct the program to exclude hours with persistent calm winds in the calculation of concentrations for each averaging period.
- Terrain-Truncation Algorithm—Terrain is automatically truncated to an elevation of .005 meter below stack top when a receptor elevation exceeds stack top elevation.
- Input Debug Option—Directs the program to print input data as soon as it is read. This option is useful for debugging input data. Note: this option differs from the Print Input Data Option, which prints input data *after* all input data has been read.
- Half-life—A non-zero value directs the program to consider pollutant decay using the input half-life in seconds.
- Wake Effects—Non-zero values for source building dimensions automatically exercise the building wake effects option. A negative value of building height or the selection of the regulatory default option directs the program to process the Schulman-Scire downwash treatment method when the physical stack height is less than or equal to the building height plus half the lesser of the height or the width (see Section 2.4.1.1.d).
- Above Ground ("flagpole") Receptor Option—directs the program to read receptor heights above local terrain elevations (this option is available regardless of the regulatory default option setting).

The ISC Long-Term (ISCLT) Model Program

The input requirements for the ISC Model long-term computer program (ISCLT) consist of four categories:

- Meteorological data.
- Source data.
- Receptor data.
- Program control parameters.

Each of these data categories is discussed separately below.

a. *Meteorological Data.* Seasonal or annual "STAR" summaries (statistical tabulations of the joint frequency of occurrence of wind-speed and wind-direction categories, classified according to the Pasquill stability categories)* are the principal meteorological inputs to ISCLT. The program accepts STAR summaries with six Pasquill stability categories (A through F) or five stability categories (A through E with the E and F categories combined). ISCLT is not designed to use the Climatological Dispersion Model (CDM) STAR day/night summaries which subdivide the neutral D stability category into day and night D categories. Additional meteorological data requirements include seasonal average maximum and minimum heights and ambient air temperatures.

b. *Source Data.* The ISCLT source data requirements are the same as those given in the previous section for the ISCST program with the exception that 16 direction-specific building dimensions, instead of 36, are required for the building wake effects for sources with certain stack heights and building dimensions.

c. *Receptor Data.* The ISCLT receptor data requirements are the same as those given in the previous section for the ISCST program.

d. *Program Control Parameters and Options.* The ISCLT program allows the user to select from a number of model and logic options. The program control parameters for these options are discussed in detail in Section 4.2.3. The available options include:

- Concentration/Deposition Option—Directs the program to calculate average concentration or total deposition.
- Receptor Grid System Option—Selects a Cartesian or a polar receptor grid system.
- Discrete Receptor Option—Allows the user to place a receptor at any point using either a Cartesian or a polar coordinate reference system.
- Receptor Terrain Elevation Option—Allows the user to specify an elevation for each receptor (level terrain is assumed by the program if this option is not exercised).

---

* STAR summaries are available from the National Climatic Data Center (NCDC), Asheville, North Carolina.

- Tape/File Input/Output Option—Directs the program to input and/or output results of all concentration or deposition calculations, source data, and meteorological data from and/or to magnetic tape or other data file.
- Print Input Option—Directs the program to print program control parameters, source data, receptor data, and meteorological data. This option prints all input data after all input data has been read.
- Print Seasonal/Annual Results Option—Directs the program to print seasonal and/or annual concentration or deposition values, where seasons are normally defined as winter, spring, summer, and fall.
- Print Results from Individual/Combined Source Option—Directs the program to print the concentration or deposition values for individual and/or combined sources, where the combined source output is the sum over a select group of sources or all sources.
- Rural/Urban Option—Specifies whether the concentration or deposition calculations are to be made in the Rural Mode, Urban Mode 1, Urban Mode 2, or Urban Mode 3 (see Section 2.2.1.1).
- Plume Rise as a Function of Distance Option—Allows the user to direct the program to calculate plume rise as a function of downwind distance or to calculate final plume rise at all downwind distances.
- Print Maximum 10/All Receptor Points Option—Specifies whether the program is to print the maximum 10 concentration (deposition) values and receptors or to print the results of the calculations at all receptors without maximums or both.
- Automatic Determination of Maximum 10 Option—Directs the program to calculate the maximum 10 values of concentration (deposition) from the set of all receptors input; also, directs the program to display the 10 values of each contributing source at the locations determined by the maximum 10 values of the combined sources or to display the maximum 10 values and locations of each source individually.
- User Specified Maximum 10 Option—Allows the user the option of specifying up to 5 sets of 10 receptor points, one set for each seasonal and annual calculation or a single set of 10 receptor points, at which each source contribution as well as the total concentration (deposition) values for the combined sources are displayed.
- Print Unit Option—Allows the user to optionally direct the print output to any output device.
- Tape/File Unit Option—Allows the user to optionally select the logical unit numbers used for magnetic tape input and output.
- Print Output Option—This option is provided to minimize paper output; if selected, the program does not start a new page with each new table, but continues printing.

- Lines per Page Option—This option is provided to enable the user to specify the exact number of lines printed per page.
- Size Options—These are parameters that allow the user to specify the number of sources input via data card, the sizes of the X and Y receptor axes if used, the number of discrete receptor points if used, the number of seasons (or annual only) in the meteorological input data, and the number of wind-speed, Pasquill stability, and wind-direction categories in the input meteorological data.
- Combined Sources Option—Allows the user the option of specifying, by source number, multiple sets of sources to use in forming combined sources output or the option of using all sources in forming combined sources output.
- Units Option—Allows the user the option of specifying the input emissions units and/or output concentration or deposition units.
- Variable Emissions Option—Allows the user the option of varying emissions by season, by wind speed and season, by Pasquill stability category and season, or by wind speed, Pasquill stability category, and season (season is either winter, spring, summer, fall or annual only).
- Stack-Tip Downwash Option—Allows the user to direct the program to use the Briggs (1974) procedures for evaluating stack-tip downwash for all sources.
- Buoyancy-Induced Dispersion Option—Allows the user to direct the program to use the Pasquill (1976) method to parameterize the growth of plumes during the plume rise phase.
- Regulatory Default Option—Allows the user to direct the program to use the following features generally recommended by EPA for regulatory applications:
  1) Final plume rise at all receptor locations.
  2) Stack-tip downwash.
  3) Buoyancy-induced dispersion.
  4) Default wind profile coefficients (urban or rural).
  5) Default vertical potential temperature gradients.
  6) A decay half life of 4 hours for SO_2, urban; otherwise the decay half life is set to infinity.
  7) Revised wake effects procedures.
  In ISCLT, all other options remain available to the user under the regulatory default option.
- Terrain-Truncation Algorithm—Terrain is automatically truncated to an elevation of .005 meter below stack top when a receptor elevation exceeds stack top elevation.
- Input Debug Option—Directs the program to print input data as soon as it is read. This option is useful for debugging input data. Note: this

option differs from the Print Input Data Option, which prints input data *after* all input data has been read.

- Half-life—A non-zero value directs the program to consider pollutant decay using the input half-life in seconds.
- Wake Effects—Non-zero values for source building dimensions automatically exercise the building wake effects option. A negative value of building height or the selection of the regulatory default option directs the program to process the Schulman-Scire downwash treatment method when the physical stack height is less than or equal to the building height plus half the lesser of the height or the width (see Section 2.4.1.1.d).
- Above Ground ("Flagpole") Receptor Option—Directs the program to read receptor heights above local terrain elevations (this option is available regardless of the regulatory default option setting).

Index